MW00365111

U.S. History
Map Activities

E. RICHARD CHURCHILL
LINDA R. CHURCHILL

J. WESTON
WALCH
PUBLISHER
Portland, Maine

User's Guide
to
Walch Reproducible Books

Purchasers of this book have permission to photocopy pages for classroom use only.

This permission is limited to a single teacher, for classroom use only.

Any questions regarding this policy or requests to purchase further reproduction rights should be addressed to:

Permissions Editor
J. Weston Walch, Publisher
321 Valley Street • P.O. Box 658
Portland, Maine 04104-0658

1   2   3   4   5   6   7   8   9   10
ISBN 0-8251-4349-7

Copyright © 1987, 2002
J. Weston Walch, Publisher
P.O. Box 658 • Portland, Maine 04104-0658
www.walch.com

Printed in the United States of America

Contents

To the Teacher

The study of history is always more meaningful when it includes geography. These map activities are designed to supplement the study of United States history, and the authors have used them successfully with students of varying abilities. With fifty reproducible maps and worksheets at hand, you can select appropriate activities for able and well-motivated students as well as for less accelerated learners. The number of activities also gives your students ample opportunity to reinforce their historical knowledge and their map-reading and research skills.

If you are using these materials for the first time, here are three helpful tips:

1. The worksheets accompanying the maps are simply suggestions. You should feel free to add or subtract items according to your individual teaching goals, the needs of your students, and the available resources.

2. Before assigning a map, check on the resources available to your students. While most of the necessary information can be found in standard American history texts or classroom atlases, some details may require students to do library research.

3. Many of the activities require students to mark regions and features in different colors. Students will need access to a variety of colored pencils.

We hope that you and your students will find these map exercises useful and enjoyable.

Map Activities

1. Early American Indians and Their Culture

1. Color the bodies of water blue and label the following:

   Atlantic Ocean   Gulf of Mexico   Gulf of California
   Pacific Ocean   Lake Superior   Lake Michigan
   Lake Huron   Lake Ontario   Lake Erie
   Lake Champlain   Puget Sound   Chesapeake Bay

2. With a blue colored pencil, trace the following rivers and label them on the map:

   Ohio   Mississippi   Susquehanna   Mohawk
   Hudson   Columbia   Colorado   Missouri
   Rio Grande   St. Lawrence

3. There were eight major American Indian cultures in the United States in 1650.

   a. Along the eastern coast were the Woodsmen of the Eastern Woodlands. On your map, color this area yellow.

   b. The next large group west of the Mississippi River was the Hunters of the Plains. On your map, color this area pink.

   c. Along the northwestern coast were the Northern Fishermen. On your map, color this area green.

   d. South of the Northern Fishermen were the Seed Gatherers. Color this area orange on your map.

   e. The smallest American Indian culture group in 1650 was the Navaho Shepherds. Color this small area red.

   f. South of the Seed Gatherers and the Navaho Shepherds in an elongated area that extends along the Rio Grande were the Desert Dwellers. Color this area purple on your map.

   g. North of the Desert Dwellers is another section of the Seed Gatherers. Color this area orange, too.

   h. Bordering the Desert Dwellers, the small area of Seed Gatherers, and the Hunters of the Plains were the Pueblo Farmers. Color this area gray.

4. The following is a partial list of American Indian tribes that lived in these eight major American Indian culture areas. On the line, write the name of the culture area to which each tribe belonged.

   Chinook _____   Pomo _____

   Shoshone _____   Apache _____

   Hopi _____   Iroquois _____

   Cherokee _____   Powhatan _____

1. Early American Indians and Their Culture

220

MILES

0

3

2. Columbus and the New World

1. Label on your map the following landmasses:

Greenland	Great Britain	Iceland	North America
Ireland	Europe	Africa	Cuba
Jamaica	Hispaniola	Puerto Rico	

2. With a dotted line, outline the country of Portugal. Locate and label Portugal and Spain on your map.

3. Place a red dot to locate these cities on your map. Label them.

   Lisbon   Palos

   a. Why was Palos important to Columbus? _____

   _____

   b. Why was Lisbon important to Columbus? _____

   _____

4. Carefully locate and label on your map the following island groups:

   Canary Islands   Azores   Bahamas

5. With an orange colored pencil, trace Columbus' first voyage to the New World.

6. What was the name of Columbus' first landing place in the New World?

   _____ Label this location on your map.

7. How many voyages did Columbus make to the New World? _____

   Trace and label each of these voyages with a pen on your map. Begin with his second voyage since his first voyage is already on the map.

8. Lightly color the water areas blue on your map.

2. Columbus and the New World

5

3. Exploration Period

1. Label the following continents on your map:

    North America   Europe   Asia
    South America   Africa   Australia

2. What does the term "mother country" mean?

    _____

    _____

3. Locate the nation of Spain. Label it on the map and color it yellow. With a yellow colored pencil, trace the voyages of the following explorers on your map. Then carefully print the explorer's name along the path of his voyage.

    Balboa   Cortés   Magellan
    Pizarro   Coronado   DeSoto

4. Locate the nation of France. Label it on the map and color it light brown. With a brown colored pencil, trace the following explorers' routes on your map. Then carefully print the explorer's name along the route of his voyage on the map.

    Champlain   Cartier   LaSalle   Marquette and Joliet

5. Locate the nation of England. Label it on the map and color it green. With a green colored pencil, trace the following explorers' routes on the map. Along the route of his voyage carefully print the explorer's name.

    Cabot   Drake   Frobisher

6. Which of these countries influenced the southern part of North America

    the most? _____

7. Which of these nations explored the eastern coast of North America first?

    _____

8. Which of the explorers on your map was the first to make his historic voyage?

    _____ In what year? _____

9. Which of the explorers on your map made the latest voyage of exploration?

    _____ What were the dates? _____

3. Exploration Period

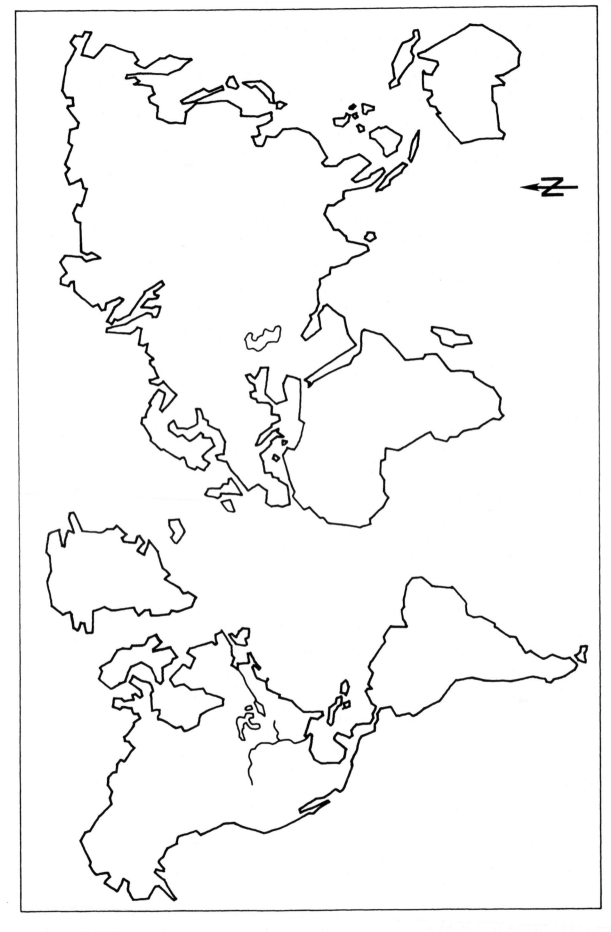

4. Colonization in North America

1. With a blue colored pencil, color the bodies of water shown on this map. Label the following neatly on your map:

   Great Lakes   Atlantic Ocean   Gulf of Mexico
   Caribbean Sea   Pacific Ocean

2. Trace the following rivers with blue and label them on the map:

   Mississippi   St. Lawrence   Colorado   Rio Grande

3. Label the following islands shown on your map:

   Cuba   Jamaica   Newfoundland
   Española   Bahamas

4. With a yellow pencil, color the Spanish Empire in North America. Locate and label the following colonies on the map:

   St. Augustine   Santa Fe   Mexico City

5. The area of New Sweden was found along Delaware Bay. Color this small area purple.

6. The area of New Netherland was found along the Hudson River. Color this area orange on your map.

7. With a brown pencil, color the French Empire in North America as of 1700.

   a. In the western part of North America, two nations claimed the same land in many places. The nations with overlapping claims were

   _____ and _____.

   b. Locate and label the following colonies on your map:

   Montreal   Quebec

8. Color the area of English colonization with a green colored pencil.

   a. England took over land colonized by which two nations?

   _____   _____

   b. Locate and label the following colonies on your map:

   Jamestown   Plymouth   Boston

4. Colonization in North America

0   600
MILES

N

5. Early English Settlement

1. Color the water areas blue on the map.

2. With a blue colored pencil, trace the following rivers and label them neatly on the map:

Savannah	Santee	Cape Fear	Roanoke
James	Potomac	Susquehanna	Delaware
Hudson	Mohawk	Connecticut	Merrimac
Kennebec			

3. With a red dot, locate each of the following early settlements on the map. Label each location.

Jamestown	Plymouth	Massachusetts Bay	Hartford
Providence	Salem	New Haven	Savannah
New York	Wilmington	Philadelphia	Charleston
Williamsburg	St. Marys	Baltimore	

4. What were the original names of these settlements?

   New York _____   Wilmington _____

5. Why did most early settlement occur along rivers or other bodies of water?

   _____

   _____

6. The first attempt at colonizing by the English was called Roanoke. Locate and label this area on your map.

   a. Why did it take the supply ship so long to return to the colony from England? _____

   _____

   b. What most likely happened to this famous "lost colony"? _____

   _____

7. There were three main types of colonies in the New World. Name one example of each form of colony found on your map.

   Proprietary colonies _____

   Royal colonies _____

   Self-governing colonies _____

5. Early English Settlement

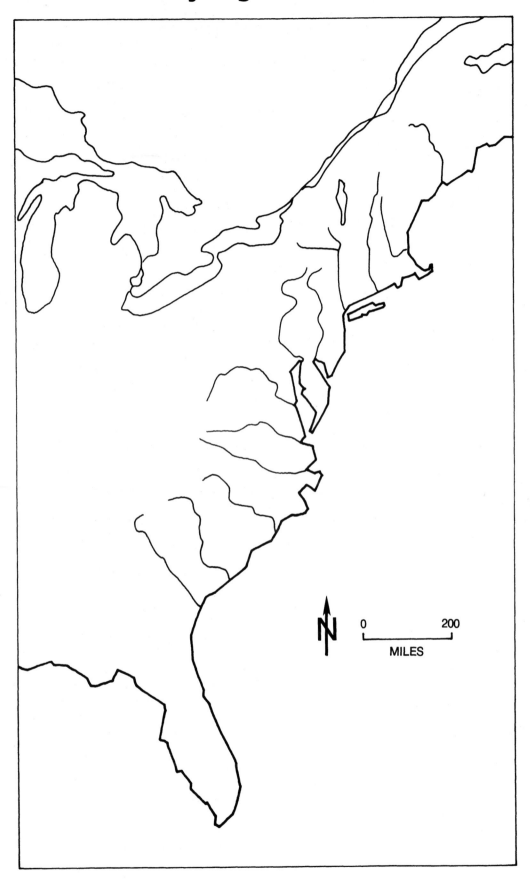

N

0   200

MILES

6. Thirteen Colonies

1. Color these water areas blue and label them on your map:

   Atlantic Ocean   Delaware Bay   Chesapeake Bay   Long Island Sound

2. Locate and label on your map the following:

   Cape Hatteras   Cape Cod   Cape Fear

3. Label the 13 English colonies on your map.

4. In Massachusetts, locate these colonial sites with a red dot. Label each location.

   Plymouth   Salem   Boston

5. Locate these colonial sites in Virginia with a red dot. Label them on the map.

   Jamestown   Williamsburg

6. Use a red dot to locate these other colonial sites on your map. Label each location.

   Providence   Hartford   New Haven   Charlestown
   Portsmouth   Philadelphia   Savannah   (Charleston)

7. Which of the original 13 colonies was the last to be settled? _____

8. With a green colored pencil, color the New England colonies.

   New Hampshire   Massachusetts   Rhode Island   Connecticut

9. With a purple colored pencil, color the Middle colonies.

   New York   Pennsylvania   New Jersey   Delaware

10. With an orange colored pencil, color the Southern colonies.

    Virginia   Maryland   North Carolina   South Carolina   Georgia

11. Many colonial claims extended beyond the borders shown on your map. Choose any two colonies and show the land they claimed west of their borders. Do this by drawing a black line to show the border they claimed.

12. What country claimed the lands west of the colonies shown on your map?

    _____ Color this area brown.

13. What country claimed the land south of Georgia? _____
    Color this area yellow.

6. Thirteen Colonies

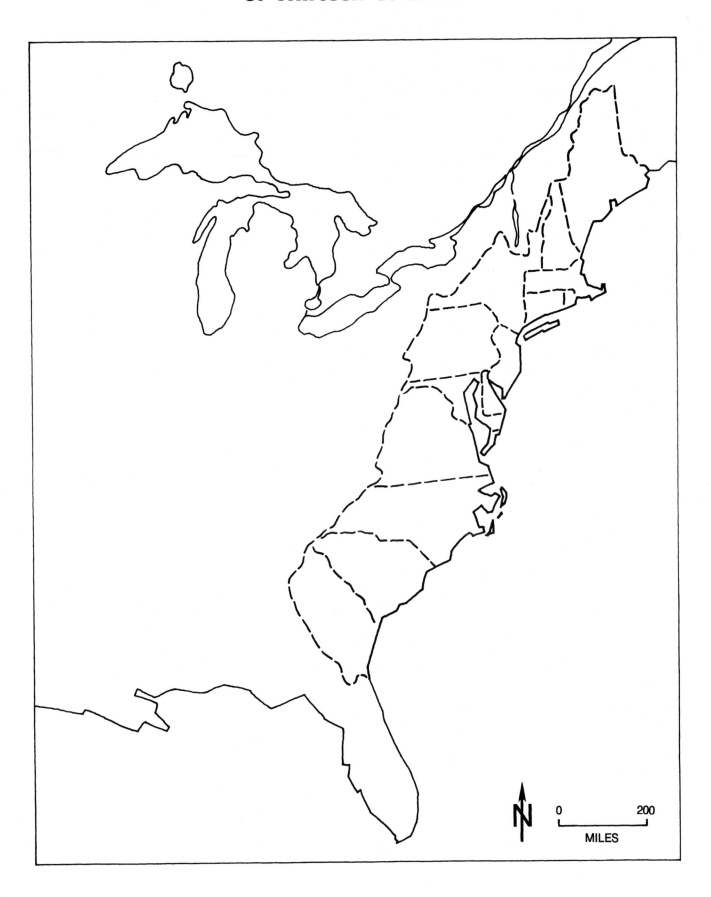

7. French and Indian War

1. Color the water areas found on this map blue and label the following:

   Atlantic Ocean   Gulf of Mexico   Pacific Ocean
   Hudson Bay   Caribbean Sea

2. Trace the following rivers with blue and label them on your map:

   Mississippi   St. Lawrence   Rio Grande
   Missouri   Colorado   Ohio
   Allegheny   Monongahela

3. Using this symbol (∧ ∧ ∧), draw in the main line of the Appalachian Mountains on your map. Use brown colored pencil.

4. Locate with a red dot the following on your map. Label each location.

   Montreal   Quebec   Boston   New York City
   Louisbourg   Ft. Duquesne   Ft. Necessity

5. What was the area called that both the English and the French wanted to control? This desire for land led to the French and Indian War.

   _____

6. What was the name of the only American Indian nation to help the English

   during the French and Indian War? _____
   With black, circle on the map the area in which these American Indians were located.

7. Color the area of English control pink on the map.

8. Color the area of French control green on your map.

9. Some areas were claimed by both England and France. Stripe this area on your map with green and pink.

7. French and Indian War

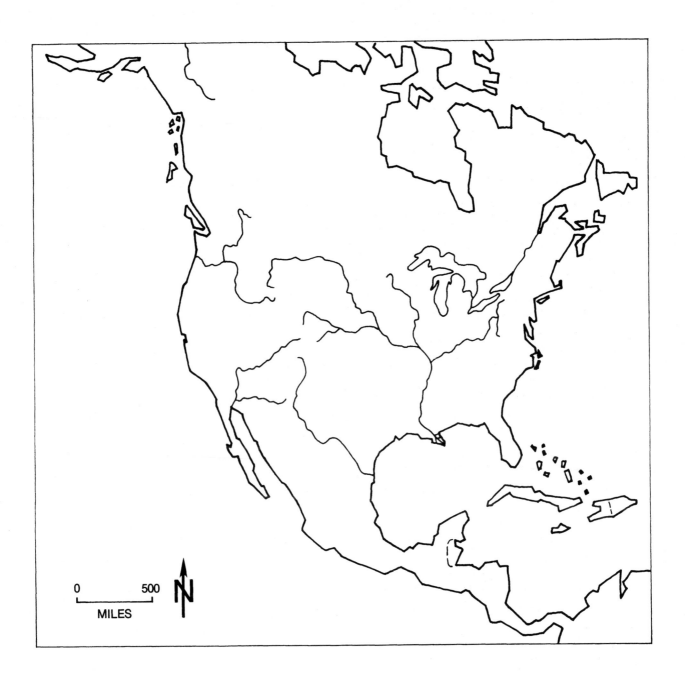

0   500
MILES

N

8. North America in 1763

1. Number the lines of latitude and longitude along the north and west sides of the map. They are shown in 10° intervals.

2. Color the bodies of water with a blue colored pencil and label the following on the map:

   Hudson Bay   Atlantic Ocean   Pacific Ocean
   Gulf of Mexico   Caribbean Sea

3. With a blue pencil, trace the following rivers and label them on the map:

   Mississippi   St. Lawrence   Missouri   Ohio

4. Show the Appalachian Mountains with brown hachures (∧ ∧ ∧) on the map.

5. Outline the territory belonging to Great Britain and color it pink.

6. Outline the territory belonging to France and color it green.

7. Outline the territory belonging to Spain and color it yellow.

8. With a red dot, locate Ft. Pitt. Label it on the map. Compare this map with the map of the French and Indian War. Answer these questions:

   a. What was Ft. Duquesne renamed? _____

   Look at a modern map of this area. What city is now located here?

   _____

   b. Who owned the territory around Hudson Bay before the French and Indian War? _____

   In 1763? _____

   c. Who owned the land west of the Mississippi before the French and Indian War? _____

   In 1763? _____

   d. Who owned Florida before the French and Indian War? _____

   In 1763? _____

9. What did the French own in 1763? _____ Label this area on the map.

8. North America in 1763

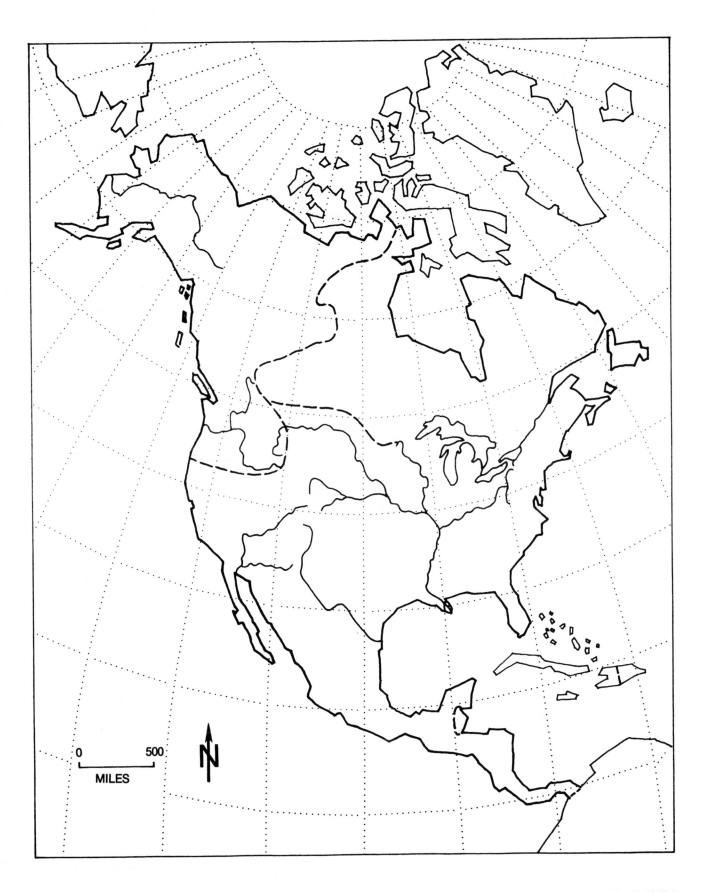

0 — 500
MILES

N

9. American Revolution

1. The latitude and longitude lines are drawn in 5° intervals. Label these on the north and west sides of the map.

2. Color the bodies of water with a blue colored pencil. Label the following bodies of water on your map:

Gulf of Mexico	Delaware Bay	Atlantic Ocean	Lake Champlain
Chesapeake Bay	Lake Ontario	Lake Huron	
Lake Erie	Lake Superior	Lake Michigan	

3. Go over the following rivers with a blue pencil and label them on the map:

Savannah	Ohio	Delaware
Wabash	Potomac	Hudson
Mississippi	Mohawk	St. Lawrence

4. Label the 13 original colonies on the map.

5. Locate the following cities with a red dot and label them on the map:

Savannah	New York City	Lexington
Charleston	Boston	Concord
Montreal	Quebec	New Orleans

6. Locate and label the following on your map:

   Valley Forge   Bunker Hill

   For what is Valley Forge remembered? _____

   _____

   For what is Bunker Hill remembered? _____

   _____

7. Battles are shown on the map with an *X*. Label these battles neatly with a pen.

8. Who controlled the land west of the Mississippi River at this time?

   _____ Color this area green.

9. Who controlled the land north of the Great Lakes? _____
   Color this area orange.

10. Continue Florida's northern border to the Mississippi River.

    Who controlled this land? _____ Color this green, too.

11. Label Cape Hatteras and Cape Cod.

 U.S. History Map Activities

9. American Revolution

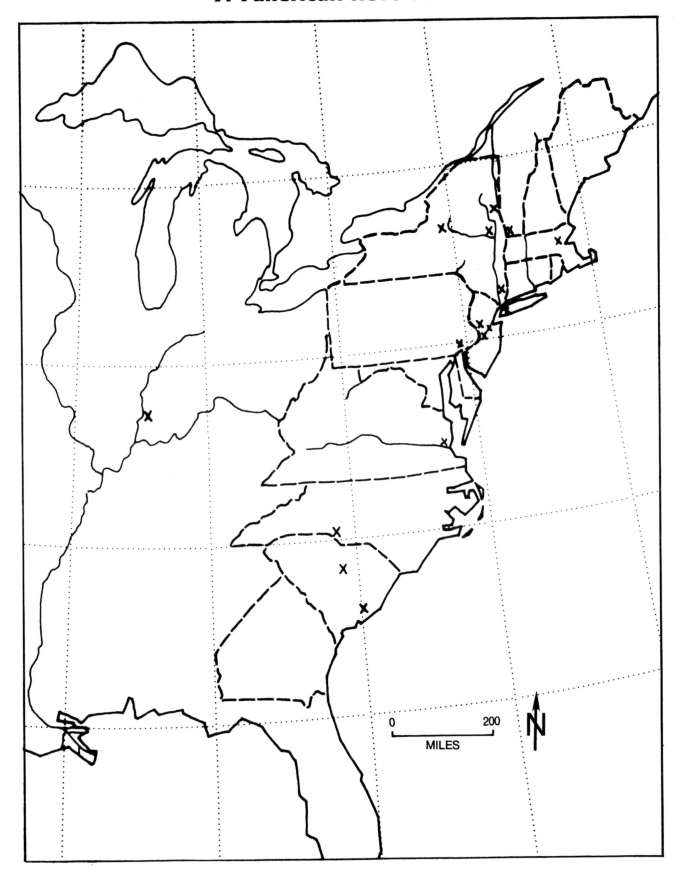

0   200
MILES

N

10. Thirteen States and the Constitution

1. Label the original 13 states on your map.

2. With a blue colored pencil, color the bodies of water on the map and label the following:

   Lake Superior   Lake Erie   Lake Ontario
   Lake Michigan   Lake Champlain   Lake Huron
   Delaware Bay   Chesapeake Bay   Atlantic Ocean

3. Trace the following rivers with a blue colored pencil. Label them on the map.

   Connecticut   Hudson   St. Lawrence   Delaware
   Potomac   Ohio   Mississippi   James
   Savannah

4. With an orange pencil, outline the Northwest Territory. This area was part of the new lands acquired after the American Revolution. Which states had claims that extended into the Northwest Territory?

   _____

   _____

5. With a red dot, locate and label the following cities on your map:

   Boston   Philadelphia   Baltimore   Richmond   Charleston

   In which of these cities did the Constitutional Convention take place?

   _____

6. The Mason-Dixon Line is the border between Pennsylvania and Maryland. Go over this line with a heavy black line.

7. Which state was the first to ratify the Constitution? _____
   Color it green on your map.

8. South of the state of Georgia lies which area? _____
   a. Who owned this area in 1789? _____
   b. Color this area yellow.
   c. Be sure to color the area west of the Mississippi River yellow as well.

9. Compare this map with a map of the East Coast today. What three states have been added to the area that had been controlled by our original thirteen states?

   _____   _____   _____

10. Thirteen States and the Constitution

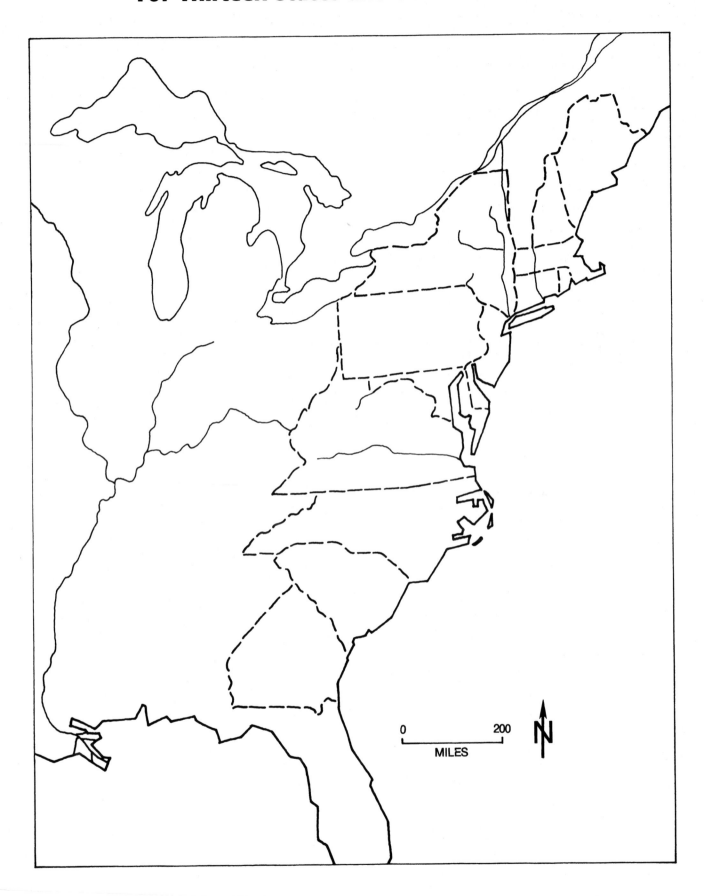

0   200
MILES

N

11. Louisiana Purchase and Western Exploration

1. Color the water areas blue and label the following on your map:

Atlantic Ocean	Pacific Ocean	Gulf of Mexico
Lake Superior	Lake Michigan	Lake Huron
Lake Ontario	Lake Erie	Lake Champlain
Great Salt Lake		

2. Label the following states on your map:

New York	Vermont	New Hampshire	Massachusetts
Connecticut	Rhode Island	New Jersey	Pennsylvania
Maryland	Delaware	Virginia	Kentucky
Ohio	Tennessee	North Carolina	South Carolina
Georgia			

3. Trace the following rivers with blue and label them on the map:

Ohio	Mississippi	Missouri	Arkansas
Red	Rio Grande	Colorado	Snake
Columbia	Yellowstone	Platte	North Platte
South Platte			

4. Locate these cities with red dots and label them on the map:

Santa Fe	New Orleans	St. Louis

5. Using the latitude and longitude lines shown on your map, draw a black line around the Louisiana Purchase.

   a. The United States bought this territory from _____.

   b. What country owned this land when the states ratified the Constitution?

   _____

6. With a red pencil, trace the route of Lewis and Clark.

7. Zebulon Pike also explored the area of the Louisiana Purchase.

   a. Trace his northern route with green.

   b. Trace his western route with brown.

   c. Place a black cross for the location of Pike's Peak. Label it on the map.

8. Color the lands claimed by Great Britain orange on your map.

9. Color the lands claimed by Spain yellow on your map.

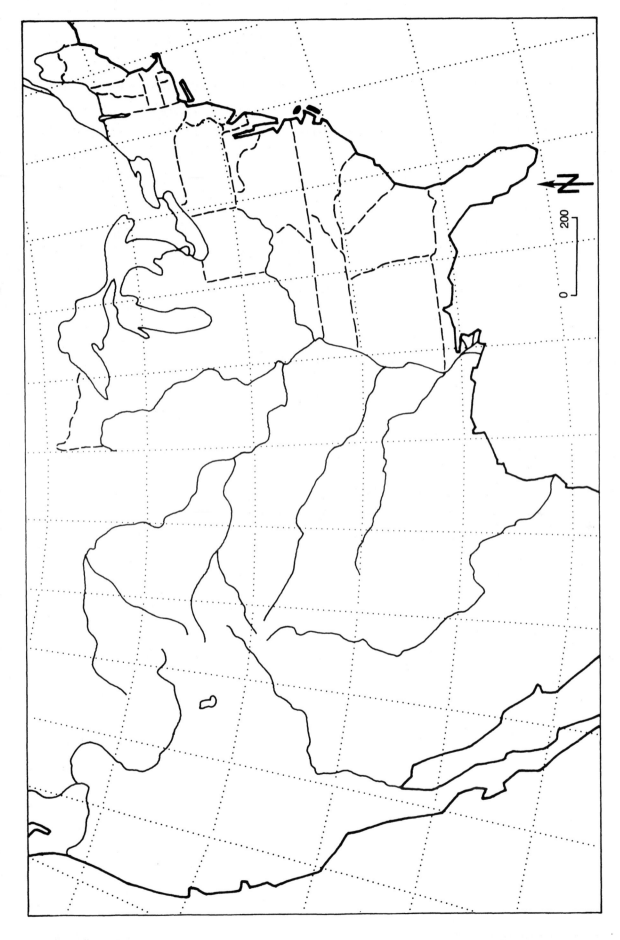

200

0

U.S. History Map Activities

12. War of 1812

1. Label the following bodies of water on your map and color them blue:

Atlantic Ocean	Lake Erie	Lake Huron
Lake Superior	Lake Michigan	Lake Ontario
Lake Champlain	Chesapeake Bay	Gulf of Mexico
Lake Pontchartrain		

2. Label the 18 states in the United States shown on your map.

3. With a blue pencil, trace the following rivers and label them on the map:

Mississippi	Ohio	Wabash	Tippecanoe
Potomac	Savannah	Alabama	St. Lawrence

4. With a red dot, locate the following cities on your map and label them:

New Orleans	Savannah	Charleston	Baltimore
Washington, D.C.	Boston	New York City	Montreal
York (Toronto)	Detroit	Erie	Quebec

5. Place a black X on the site and label each of the following battles:

New Orleans	Horseshoe Bend	Tippecanoe	Washington
Lake Erie	Plattsburg	Ft. McHenry	Battle of the Thames

   a. General William Henry Harrison earned a nickname because of which

      battle? _____

   b. What was unusual about the battle of New Orleans? _____

      _____

6. What nation controlled Florida at this time? _____
   Color this area yellow on your map.

7. What nation controlled Canada at this time? _____
   Color this area pink on your map.

8. Draw a black line to show the British blockade on your map.

12. War of 1812

0   200
MILES

N

   U.S. History Map Activities

13. Settlement of Northwest Territory

1. Color the water areas blue and label the following on your map:

   Lake Superior   Lake Michigan   Lake Huron
   Lake Erie   Lake Ontario

2. Trace the following rivers with blue and label them on your map:

   Mississippi   Missouri   Illinois
   Wabash   Tippecanoe   Ohio
   Miami   Muskingum   Allegheny
   Monongahela   Cumberland   Tennessee

3. Place a red dot on the map where each of these settlements was found.
   Label each.

   Pittsburgh   Cleveland   Marietta
   Detroit   Cincinnati   Ft. Dearborn
   St. Louis

   a. This was the first permanent U.S. settlement in Ohio.

   _____

   b. Today Ft. Dearborn is known as _____.

   c. Look at the location of the settlements you have placed on your map.
      What do they have in common? _____

   _____

4. How did the farmers living in the Northwest Territory get their crops to the

   cities on the East Coast? _____

   _____

   _____

5. Label the five states on this map that were admitted between 1803
   and 1848.

13. Settlement of Northwest Territory

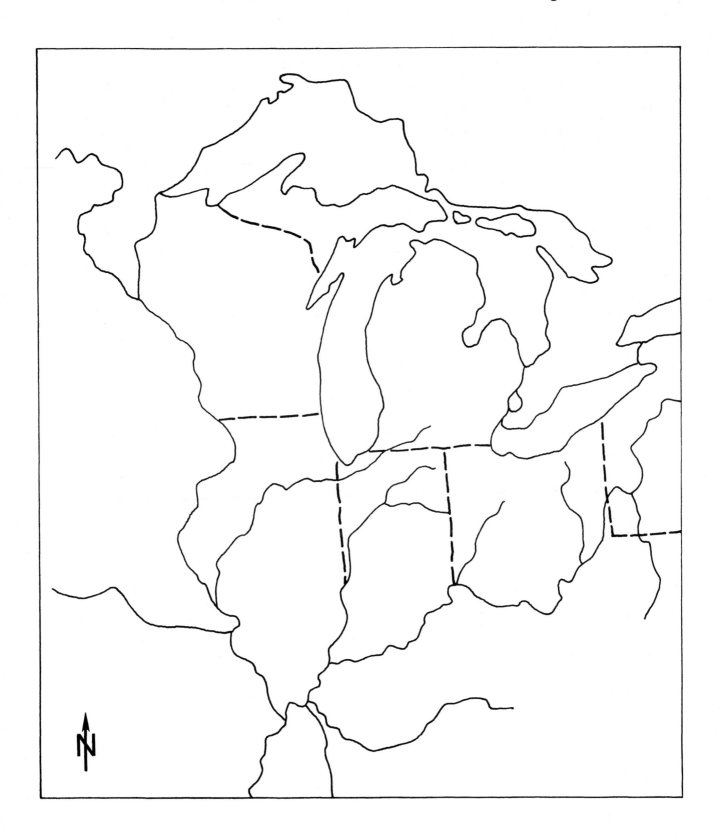

14. Expansion of United States to 1833

1. The latitude and longitude lines are drawn in 5° intervals. Label these on the north and west sides of the map.

2. Label the states in the United States as of 1803:

Georgia	North Carolina	Maryland	Ohio
South Carolina	Virginia	Delaware	New Jersey
New York	Connecticut	Rhode Island	Kentucky
Massachusetts	Vermont	New Hampshire	Tennessee
Pennsylvania			

3. Trace in blue and label the following rivers:

Mississippi	Mohawk	Hudson	Ohio
Monongahela	Tennessee	Cumberland	Allegheny

4. Color the bodies of water blue and label the following:

Lake Erie	Atlantic Ocean	Gulf of Mexico	Lake Huron
Lake Ontario	Lake Champlain	Lake Michigan	Lake Superior

5. With brown hachures (∧ ∧ ∧), show the Appalachian Mountains.

6. There were three main routes across the Appalachian Mountains:

   a. The northern route followed the Mohawk River from the Hudson River toward Lake Erie. Then it followed the Allegheny River. Draw this route with green arrows. This route was called the Genesee Road.

   b. The southern route started in South Carolina. It traveled east of the Appalachian Mountains into Georgia. Then it went around the mountains into the area of Alabama. Draw this route with yellow arrows.

   c. The middle route went through the Cumberland Gap. Find this gap on your map. The road was called the Wilderness Road. Draw this route with red arrows.

7. What states became states between 1803 and 1833? Label them on the map.

   _____

8. Who owned Florida by 1833? _____

9. What areas east of the Mississippi were not states by 1833? _____

   _____

   Color these areas brown.

14. Expansion of United States to 1833

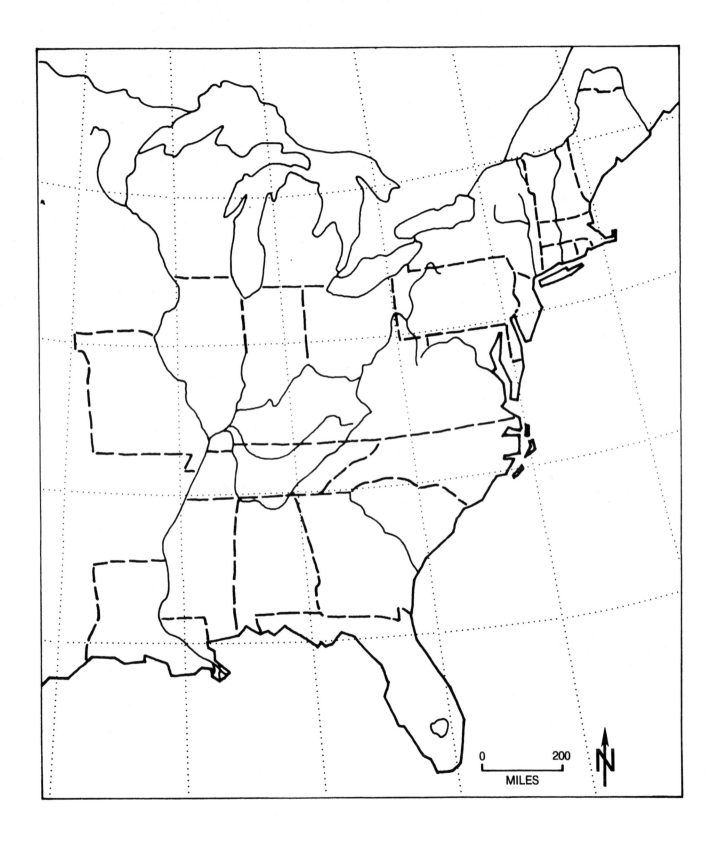

0   200
MILES

N

15. United States Before the Civil War

1. The latitude and longitude lines are drawn in 5° intervals. Label these on the north and west sides of the map.

2. Trace the following rivers in blue and label them on the map:

    Mississippi   Potomac   Ohio   Savannah

3. Go over the Mason-Dixon Line heavily with a black colored pencil.

4. On your map, label the states in 1860.

5. Outline in red the two states that became states as a result of the Missouri Compromise of 1820.

6. Outline in green the state that became a state as a result of the Compromise of 1850.

7. Use yellow to color the areas and states that were to be free of slavery.

8. With gray pencil, color the areas and states that were to allow slavery.

9. What formed the border between slave and free states east of the Mississippi

    River? _____

    and _____

10. What was the border between slave and free territories west of the Mississippi

    River? _____

    _____

11. What state was the exception to this line west of the Mississippi?

    _____

12. What three states became states during the Civil War?

    _____   _____   _____

    Label these on the map.

15. United States Before the Civil War

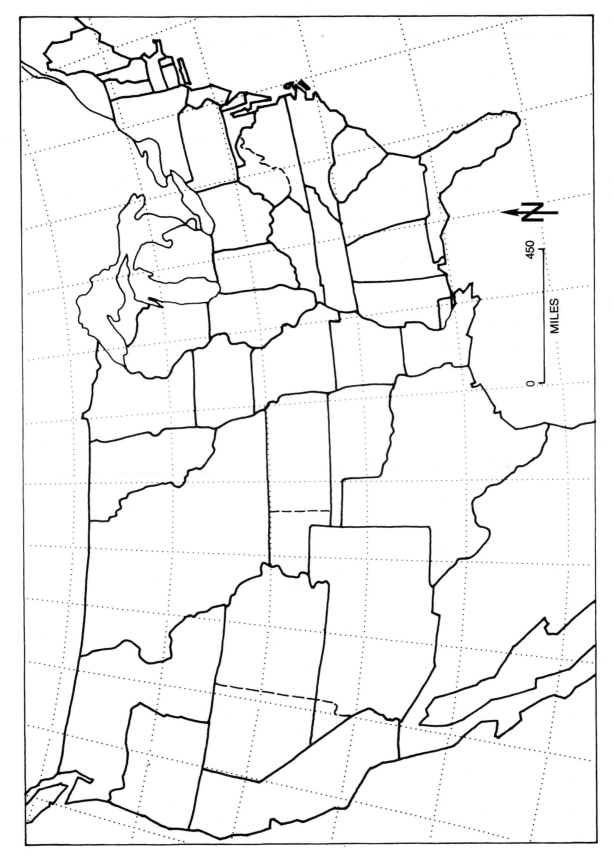

MILES

0

450

N

© 1987, 2002 J. Weston Walch, Publisher

16. Texas and the Mexican War

1. Label the following bodies of water on your map. Shade them blue.

   Gulf of Mexico   Pacific Ocean   Atlantic Ocean
   Gulf of California   Caribbean Sea

2. With a blue colored pencil, trace and label the following rivers on your map:

   Grande de Santiago   Rio Grande   Colorado   San Joaquin
   Gila   Nueces   Red   Sacramento
   Arkansas   Missouri   Mississippi   Snake
   Ohio   Columbia

3. With a red dot, locate and label the following on the map:

   New Orleans   San Antonio   Monterrey   Buena Vista
   Mexico City   Veracruz   Guadalupe Hidalgo   Santa Fe
   San Diego   Los Angeles   Monterey   San Francisco
   Sonoma   St. Louis   Ft. Leavenworth

4. With an orange pencil, trace Kearny's route from Ft. Leavenworth to Santa Fe,
   to San Diego, to Los Angeles.

   Who joined Kearny in San Diego? _____
   Trace his route with yellow from Sonoma to Monterey, to San Diego.

5. Outline the area of the Republic of Texas with a black line.

   a. The area between the Nueces and the Rio Grande was claimed by both
      Mexico and the Republic of Texas. Stripe this area with pink and green.

   b. Color the remaining area of the Republic of Texas green.

6. With a purple pencil, trace Scott's route from New Orleans to Veracruz to
   Mexico City.

7. With a brown pencil, trace Taylor's route from the Nueces to Monterrey, and
   on to Buena Vista.

8. The treaty that ended the Mexican War was called the Treaty of

   _____.

9. Color the area pink that remained Mexico after the treaty was signed.

16. Texas and the Mexican War

N

33

17. Territorial Acquisitions

1. With blue, color and label these bodies of water:

Atlantic Ocean	Pacific Ocean	Gulf of Mexico
Gulf of California	Lake Erie	Lake Ontario
Lake Superior	Lake Huron	Lake Michigan

2. Trace the following rivers with blue and label them on the map:

Ohio	Mississippi	Missouri	Colorado
Rio Grande	Columbia	Yellowstone	Arkansas
Platte			

3. Color the area of the original 13 states dark green.

4. Color the land acquired in the treaty of 1783 light green.

5. In 1803, the United States bought the Louisiana Territory from

   _____.

6. Label and date the following sections acquired by the United States:

West Florida	Florida	Mexican Cession
Texas	Gadsden Purchase	Oregon Country

   Area ceded by Great Britain

   a. At one time the Oregon Country was claimed by four nations. These nations

      were _____, _____, _____,

      and _____.

   b. The United States finally acquired the Oregon Country from

      _____.

   c. The United States acquired the area of Florida in sections. From whom was

      Florida acquired? _____

   d. The United States acquired an area of land from France. What was this

      area called? _____

7. When was Alaska acquired? _____

8. When was Hawaii acquired? _____

17. Territorial Acquisitions

N

0   220
MILES

18. The Way West

1. The latitude and longitude lines are drawn in 5° intervals. Label these on the north and west sides of the map.

2. Color the bodies of water blue and label the following:

Atlantic Ocean	Pacific Ocean	Gulf of Mexico
Great Lakes	Gulf of California	Great Salt Lake

3. Trace the following rivers with a blue pencil and label them on the map:

Mississippi	Missouri	Ohio	Colorado
Columbia	Arkansas	Rio Grande	

4. Using the beginnings of the rivers as a guide, draw in the main chain of the Rocky Mountains with hachures (∧ ∧ ∧) in pencil.

5. Locate with a red dot and label the following cities on the map:

   a. St. Louis, San Diego, San Francisco, Sacramento
      Connect these cities with a brown line. This was the route of the Butterfield Overland Mail. Label it on the map.

   b. Independence, Santa Fe
      Connect these cities with a yellow line. Label this the Santa Fe Trail.

   c. Omaha, Laramie, Portland
      Connect these cities with a black line. Label this the Oregon Trail.

   d. Just north of the Great Salt Lake started a branch trail to Sacramento. Color this trail with purple and label it the California Trail.

   e. The Mormon Trail followed the Oregon Trail until it branched off to go to Salt Lake. Label Salt Lake City and go over the short Mormon Trail with green.

6. For a short time in our history, the Pony Express was important. Locate with a red dot and label St. Joseph. Connect the cities of San Francisco, Sacramento, Salt Lake City, Laramie, and St. Joseph with ink. Label the Pony Express on the map.

18. The Way West

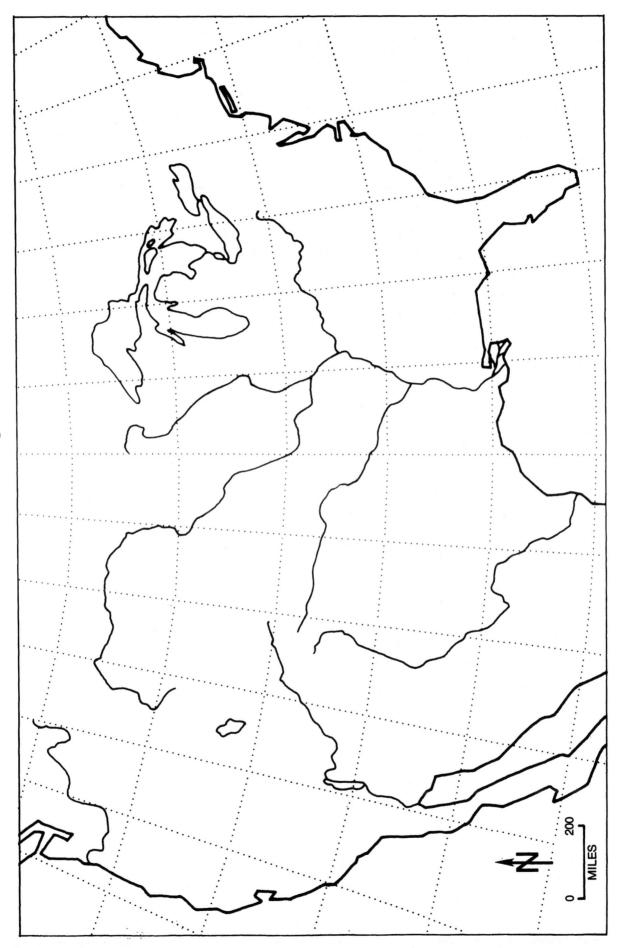

37

MILES

200

0

19. Mining Regions and Cattle Trails of the Old West

1. Color the water areas blue and label the following on your map:

Pacific Ocean	Gulf of California	Great Salt Lake
Lake Superior	Lake Michigan	Gulf of Mexico

2. With blue, trace the following rivers and label them on your map:

Columbia	Snake	Missouri	Yellowstone
Mississippi	North Platte	South Platte	Platte
Arkansas	Red	Sabine	Brazos
Nueces	Pecos	Rio Grande	Gila
Colorado	Humboldt	San Joaquin	Sacramento
American			

3. Using this symbol (∧ ∧ ∧) and a brown pencil, draw in and label the main chain of the following mountain ranges:

Sierra Nevada	Cascade	Bitterroot	Rocky

4. Locate the following settlements or mining areas on your map with a red dot. Label each carefully.

Sutter's Fort	Virginia City	Tombstone	Kansas City
Silver City	Silverton	Central City	Lead
Helena	Cheyenne	Boise	Pueblo
San Antonio	Dodge City	Abilene	

5. Label the following states on your map:

Texas	Oklahoma	Kansas	Missouri
New Mexico	Colorado	Wyoming	Nebraska
South Dakota	Montana		

6. With an orange pencil, trace the Shawnee Trail from San Antonio to Kansas City.

7. Use a green pencil to trace the Chisholm Trail from San Antonio to Abilene.

8. The Goodnight-Loving Trail went from central Texas to New Mexico and then north to Cheyenne. Draw this trail with purple on the map.

9. Label the states on the map that have not already been named.

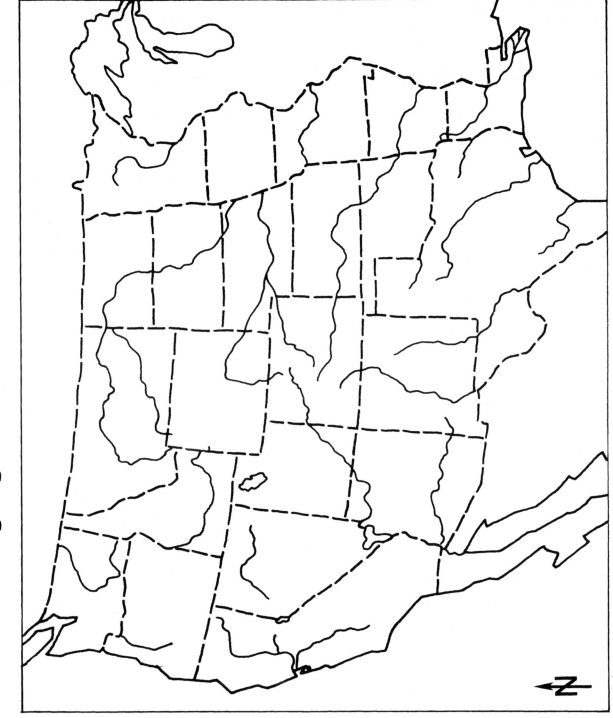

20. War Between the States

1. The latitude and longitude lines are drawn in 5° intervals. Label these on the north and west sides of the map.

2. With a blue colored pencil, color the water areas and label the following:

Lake Michigan	Lake Ontario	Lake Erie	Lake Huron
Atlantic Ocean	Chesapeake Bay	Gulf of Mexico	

3. Trace the following rivers with a blue colored pencil and label them on the map.

Mississippi	Potomac	Ohio	Savannah

4. Label the states shown on your map.

5. Draw a heavy black line separating the states that allowed slavery from those that did not allow slavery.

6. Label the following cities on your map:

New Orleans	Montgomery	Washington, D.C.	Vicksburg
Atlanta	Richmond	Savannah	

7. Which two of these cities served as capital of the Confederate States of America? _____ and _____

8. Locate and label the following:

Gettysburg	Appomattox Court House	Antietam

9. The Union capital was surrounded by land held by what slave-holding state?

   _____

10. Color gray the eleven Confederate States of America.

11. With a dotted black line, show the Union blockade of Southern shipping.

12. Lee invaded the Northern states two times. He was stopped at two famous battles. Name them.

    _____ and _____

13. Show the route of Sherman's march to the sea with a heavy red line.

14. The official surrender of the Confederate Army under General Lee occurred at

    _____.

20. War Between the States

U.S. History Map Activities

21. Overseas America 1867–1940

1. The latitude lines are drawn in 20° intervals. Go over the equator with a red colored pencil and label the latitude lines on the east side of the map.

2. The longitude lines are drawn in 20° intervals. Label these on the north side of the map. Go over the International Date Line with a brown colored pencil. The International Date Line closely follows the _____ longitude line.

3. Label the United States. Color the 48 contiguous states with a green colored pencil.

   a. The first territory added to the United States as a possession was

      _____ in 1867. Label and date this area on your map.

   b. In 1867, the United States acquired Midway Island. Locate and label this island in the Pacific Ocean.

   c. In 1898, the United States added the Hawaiian Islands, Wake Island, and Guam Islands. Locate and label these on the map.

4. In 1898, the United States and Spain fought the Spanish-American War. As a result, the United States added the following three territories:

   Philippine Islands   Puerto Rico   Cuba

   Locate and label all three on the map. Which of these three is still controlled

   by the United States? _____

5. In 1904, the United States took charge of the Canal Zone in Panama. Draw in the Panama Canal and label it on the map.

6. In 1917, the United States bought the Virgin Islands from Denmark. Label these on the map.

7. Throughout the years 1867 to 1940, the United States gained many islands in the Pacific. Locate, using latitude and longitude, and label any three of the following:

   Johnston Island   Samoa Island   Howland Island
   Tutuila Island   Baker Island   Jarvis Island
   Canton Island   Christmas Island   Enderbury Island
   Palmyra Island

21. Overseas America 1867–1940

N

2000

MILES

0

U.S. History Map Activities

22. Spanish-American War

1. Locate and label the following countries on your map:

United States	Bahamas	Mexico	Guatemala
British Honduras	Honduras	El Salvador	Nicaragua
(Belize)	Panama	Jamaica	Colombia
Costa Rica	Cuba	Haiti	Dominican
Venezuela			Republic
Puerto Rico			

2. Use a red dot to locate each of these cities on your map. Label each location.

Tampa	Havana	Santiago	San Juan
Miami	New Orleans	Kingston	Port-au-Prince

   a. What event occurred in Havana that caused Americans to be extremely angry? _____

   _____

   b. The most famous land battle of the Spanish-American War occurred outside the city of _____. This battle was called _____. Locate this site on your map and label it.

3. Locate and label the following bodies of water on your map:

Atlantic Ocean	Gulf of Mexico	Caribbean Sea
Pacific Ocean	Straits of Florida	Old Bahama Channel

4. With a yellow pencil, show the route of the U.S. Army to Cuba. Where else did the U.S. Army invade? _____

5. With a black line, show the United States blockade on your map.

6. The United States gained new territory by the terms of the treaty that ended the Spanish American War. List these areas.

   _____   _____   _____

7. What happened to Cuba after the war? _____

   _____

8. The United States naval base on Cuba is called _____.

22. Spanish-American War

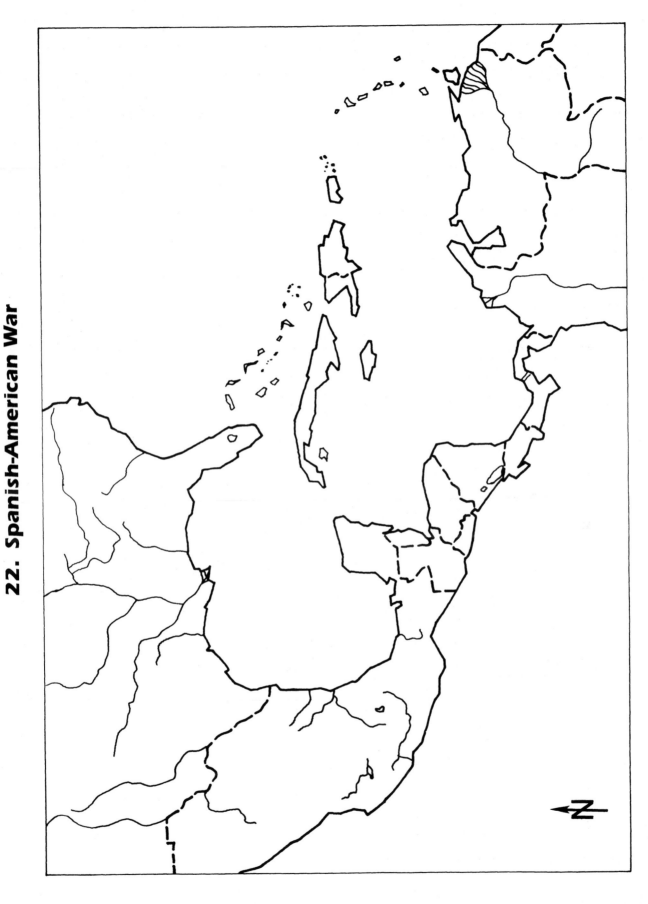

23. World War I

1. Color the water areas of this map lightly with a blue pencil and label the following:

Baltic Sea	North Sea	Caspian Sea
Mediterranean Sea	English Channel	Black Sea
Strait of Gibraltar		

2. On the map, label each of the following countries:

Belgium	Denmark	Great Britain	Greece
Romania	Germany	Norway	France
Ottoman Empire (Turkey)	Austria-Hungary	Italy	Serbia
	Russia	Bulgaria	Netherlands
Albania	Luxembourg	Switzerland	Spain
Sweden	Montenegro		
Portugal			

3. Outline the boundaries of those nations that were members of the Triple Entente with purple.

4. Outline the boundaries of those nations that were members of the Triple Alliance with pink.

5. The *Lusitania* was sunk off the southern coast of Ireland. Locate this spot and mark it with a red star.

6. Outline the Balkan peninsula with a heavy black line.

7. With a brown pencil, draw in the route of the proposed Berlin to Baghdad Railroad.

8. Shade with pink those nations that fought on the side of the Central Powers.

9. Shade with purple those nations that fought on the side of the Allies.

10. With an orange dotted line, draw the British blockade.

11. Color yellow those nations that remained neutral.

12. Color the area of German submarine activity dark blue.

13. When the United States entered World War I, it joined the _____ Powers.

23. World War I

MILES

0   400

N

24. World War II in the Pacific

1. The latitude and longitude lines are shown in 20° intervals. Label these on the north and west sides of the map. Be sure to put north and south latitude and east and west longitude on the map, too.

2. Go over the equator with red.

3. Neatly label the following countries or island groups on the map:

Australia	Borneo	Aleutian Islands
China	Formosa (Taiwan)	Korea
Philippines	Hawaiian Islands	Japan
New Zealand	New Guinea	Dutch East Indies
Manchuria		

4. Using the latitude and longitude directions given, locate and label the following individual islands:

Okinawa	26° N latitude	129° E longitude
Iwo Jima	22° N latitude	141° E longitude
Wake	26° N latitude	165° E longitude
Midway	28° N latitude	178° E longitude

5. Lightly color the bodies of water blue and label the following:

   Coral Sea   Pacific Ocean   Atlantic Ocean   Indian Ocean

6. Label the area that was French Indo-China.

7. The Gilbert Islands are located from 5° N latitude to 10° S latitude and from 170° E longitude to 180° W longitude. Locate these on the map and label them.

8. Color with yellow the fullest extent of Japanese control during World War II.

9. Put a small red *X* where Hiroshima and Nagasaki are located.

10. Locate Pearl Harbor with an *X* and label it on the map. Was this captured by

    the Japanese? _____

11. The Alcan Highway was built from March to October 1942, from Dawson Creek, British Columbia, to Fairbanks, Alaska. Draw this road on your map.

    Why was it built? _____

    _____

24. World War II in the Pacific

U.S. History Map Activities

N

MILES:
0   2000

25. American Involvement in Vietnam

1. With a blue pencil, color the water areas on your map. Label the following:

   Gulf of Tonkin   Gulf of Siam   South China Sea
                              (Gulf of Thailand)

2. Label the following countries on the map:

   Burma   Thailand   Cambodia
   Laos   China   North Vietnam
   South Vietnam

3. Trace the Mekong River with dark blue and label it on the map.

   This river forms almost the entire western border of _____.

4. Label the island of Hainan on your map. Which country controls it?

   _____

5. Locate the following cities with a red dot and label them on the map:

   Vientiane   Hanoi   Saigon (Hô Chi Minh
   Bangkok   Phnom Penh   City)
   Vinh   Pleiku

6. Make a red square on your map to show where the following United States bases were located:

   Huê   Dă Nâng   Quang Ngai   Qui Nhon   Cam Ranh Bay

7. As closely as possible, draw in the Demilitarized Zone (DMZ) with a black line.

   What does *demilitarize* mean? _____

   _____

8. The Hô Chi Minh Trail is shown on your map with this symbol (╈╈╈╈╈╈). Label it on the map.

9. Draw a brown circle around the Mekong Delta.

10. Color with a green pencil the nations allied with the United States.

11. With a pink pencil, color the Communist nations.

25. American Involvement in Vietnam

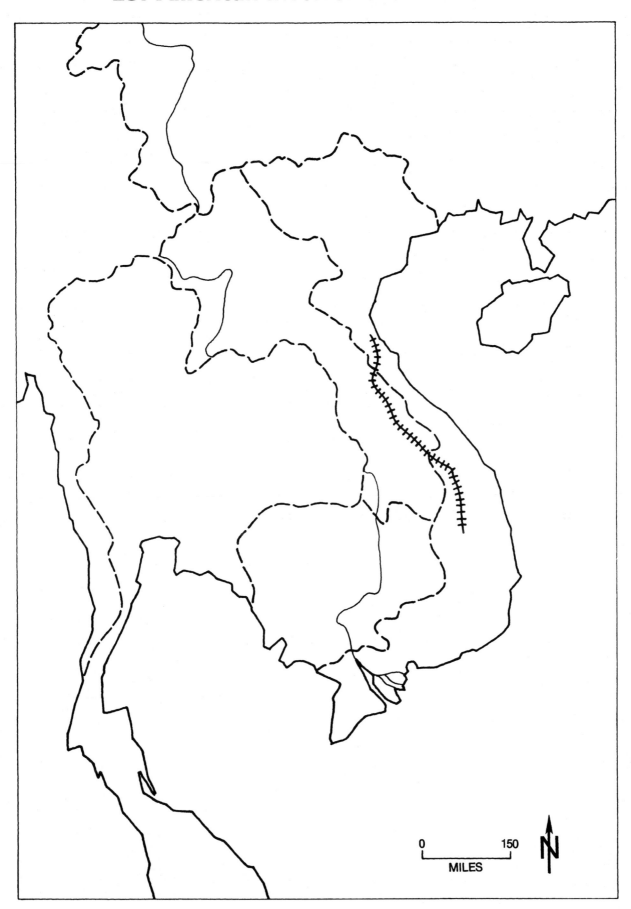

0   150

MILES

N

Answer Key

Answer Key

WORKSHEET 1

Early American Indians and Their Culture

4. Chinook—Northern Fishermen
    Pomo—Seed Gatherers
    Shoshone—Hunters of the Plains
    Apache—Desert Dwellers
    Hopi—Pueblo Farmers
    Iroquois—Northern Eastern Woodlands
    Cherokee—Southern Eastern Woodlands
    Powhatan—Chesapeake Bay area of Eastern Woodlands

WORKSHEET 2

Columbus and the New World

3. a. He set sail from here on August 3,1492.
    b. Columbus landed here before his return to Palos in 1493.
6. San Salvador
7. Four

WORKSHEET 3

Exploration Period

2. The country from which an explorer comes or the sponsoring nation of an explorer
6. Spain
7. England
8. Cabot, 1497
9. LaSalle, 1679–82

WORKSHEET 4

Colonization in North America

7. a. Spain, France
8. a. Netherlands (New Amsterdam), Sweden (New Sweden)

WORKSHEET 5

Early English Settlement

4. New Amsterdam   Ft. Christina
5. For easy transportation; supplies came by ship from Europe.
6. a. Ships and men were needed to defeat the Spanish Armada.
   b. Answers will vary. The most likely may include: "The colonists went to live with American Indians," or "Members of the colony were killed by American Indians."
7. Proprietary: Pennsylvania, Maryland, the Carolinas
   Royal: Virginia, Massachusetts, New Hampshire
   Self-governing: Connecticut, Rhode Island

WORKSHEET 6

Thirteen Colonies

3. Georgia   South Carolina   North Carolina   Virginia
   Maryland   Delaware   Pennsylvania   New Jersey
   New York   Rhode Island   Connecticut   Massachusetts
   New Hampshire
7. Georgia
12. France
13. Spain

WORKSHEET 7

French and Indian War

5. Ohio Valley
6. Iroquois

WORKSHEET 8

North America in 1763

8. a. Fort Pitt, Pittsburgh
   b. Great Britain, Great Britain
   c. France, Spain
   d. Spain, Great Britain
9. Haiti

WORKSHEET 9

American Revolution

4. Georgia   South Carolina   North Carolina   Virginia
   Maryland   Delaware   Pennsylvania   New Jersey
   New York   Rhode Island   Connecticut   Massachusetts
   New Hampshire
6. Valley Forge: George Washington's troops wintered here in 1777.
   Bunker Hill: Site of a famous battle near Boston at the beginning of the war
7. New York: Saratoga, Ft. Ticonderoga, Oriskany, West Point, New York City
   Massachusetts: Boston
   Vermont Area: Bennington
   Pennsylvania: Brandywine
   New Jersey: Princeton, Morristown, Trenton
   Virginia: Yorktown
   North Carolina: Kings Mountain
   South Carolina: Camden, Charleston
   Northwest Territory: Ft. Vincennes
8. Spain
9. Great Britain
10. Spain

WORKSHEET 10

Thirteen States and the Constitution

1. Georgia   South Carolina   North Carolina   Virginia
   Maryland   Delaware   Pennsylvania   New Jersey
   New York   Rhode Island   Connecticut   Massachusetts
   New Hampshire
4. Virginia, New York, Connecticut, Massachusetts
5. Philadelphia
7. Delaware
8. Florida
   a. Spain
9. Maine, Vermont, West Virginia

WORKSHEET 11

Louisiana Purchase and Western Exploration

5. a. France
   b. Spain

WORKSHEET 12

War of 1812

5. a. Tippecanoe
   b. The War of 1812 was already over when this battle took place.
6. Spain
7. Great Britain

WORKSHEET 13

Settlement of Northwest Territory

3. a. Marietta
   b. Chicago
   c. Settled along bodies of water
4. Floated them down rivers to New Orleans and then by boat through the Gulf of Mexico to the Atlantic Ocean

WORKSHEET 14

Expansion of United States to 1833

7. Ohio   Indiana   Illinois   Maine
   Louisiana   Mississippi   Alabama   Missouri
8. United States
9. Florida   Wisconsin   Michigan
   Minnesota   West Virginia

WORKSHEET 15

United States Before the Civil War

4. Delaware   Connecticut   New Hampshire   Rhode Island
   Massachusetts   Vermont   Maine   New Jersey
   Pennsylvania   New York   Maryland   North Carolina
   South Carolina   Georgia   Florida   Alabama
   Virginia   Louisiana   Kentucky   Tennessee
   Mississippi   Arkansas   Indiana   Michigan
   Wisconsin   Ohio   Iowa   Illinois
   Minnesota   Missouri   Texas   Oregon
   California
5. Maine, Missouri
6. California
9. Mason-Dixon Line
   Ohio River
10. Southern border of Missouri (36° 30') in the Louisiana Purchase (due to the Missouri Compromise)
11. Missouri
12. West Virginia, Nevada, Kansas

WORKSHEET 16

Texas and the Mexican War

4. Frémont
8. Guadalupe Hidalgo

WORKSHEET 17

Territorial Acquisitions

3. Delaware   New Jersey   Georgia   Connecticut
   South Carolina   Pennsylvania   Virginia   Massachusetts
   North Carolina   New Hampshire   Maryland   New York
   Rhode Island
4. All the land between the Appalachian Mountains and the Mississippi River from the Great Lakes south to Florida
5. France
6. a. Spain, Russia, United States, Great Britain
   b. Great Britain
   c. Spain
   d. Louisiana Purchase
7. 1867
8. 1898

WORKSHEET 19

Mining Regions and Cattle Trails of the Old West

9. | Washington | Oregon | California | Nevada |
|---|---|---|---|
| Arizona | Utah | Idaho | North Dakota |
| Minnesota | Iowa | Arkansas | Louisiana |

WORKSHEET 20

War Between the States

5. Slave states:

Delaware	Maryland	Virginia	Georgia
Louisiana	Alabama	Arkansas	Tennessee
South Carolina	North Carolina	Florida	Texas
Mississippi	Missouri	Kentucky	

7. Montgomery, Alabama; Richmond, Virginia
9. Maryland
10. | Texas | Louisiana | Arkansas | Mississippi |
|---|---|---|---|
| Alabama | Tennessee | Georgia | Florida |
| Virginia | South Carolina | North Carolina | |

11. The coastline from Virginia south around Florida and into the Gulf of Mexico to southern Texas
12. Gettysburg, Pennsylvania; Antietam, Maryland
14. Appomattox Court House, Virginia

WORKSHEET 21

Overseas America 1867–1940

2. 180°
3. a. Alaska
4. Puerto Rico

WORKSHEET 22

Spanish-American War

2. a. Sinking of the battleship *Maine*
   b. Santiago, San Juan Hill
4. Puerto Rico
6. Puerto Rico, Guam, Philippines
7. Spain gave up claim to Cuba. Cuba became independent in 1902.
8. Guantanamo Bay

WORKSHEET 23

World War I

3. Great Britain, France, Russia
4. Germany, Austria-Hungary, Italy
8. Germany, Austria-Hungary, Bulgaria, Turkey
9. Belgium   Serbia   Great Britain   Russia
   Greece   Romania   France   Portugal
   Italy   Montenegro   Luxembourg
11. Denmark   Netherlands   Norway   Albania
    Sweden   Switzerland   Spain
13. Allied

WORKSHEET 24

World War II in the Pacific

8. Indo-China   Dutch East Indies   Eastern China
   Korea   Pacific Islands   All of Manchuria
10. No
11. To supply Alaska in case it was invaded by the Japanese

WORKSHEET 25

American Involvement in Vietnam

3. Laos
4. China
7. To deprive of military character; free from militarism
10. South Vietnam, Thailand
11. China, North Vietnam

Map 1: Early American Indians and Their Culture

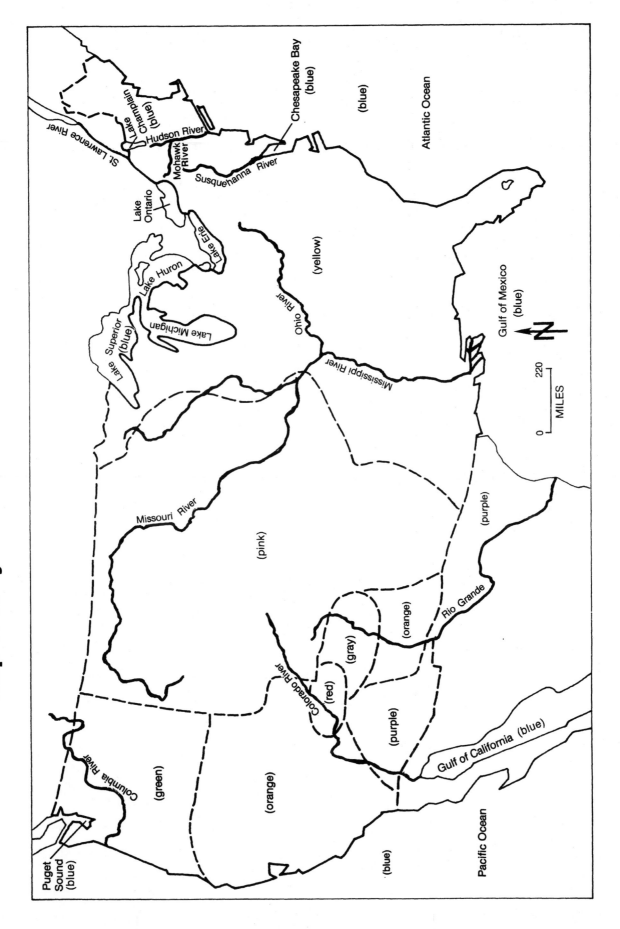

St. Lawrence River

Lake Champlain (blue)

Hudson River

Mohawk River

Chesapeake Bay (blue)

(blue)

Atlantic Ocean

Susquehanna River

Lake Ontario

Lake Erie

Lake Huron

(yellow)

Lake Superior (blue)

Lake Michigan

Ohio River

Gulf of Mexico (blue)

Mississippi River

N

220

MILES

0

Missouri River

(pink)

(purple)

(orange)

Rio Grande

(gray)

Colorado River

(red)

(purple)

(orange)

(green)

Columbia River

Gulf of California (blue)

(blue)

Puget Sound (blue)

Pacific Ocean

Map 2: Columbus and the New World

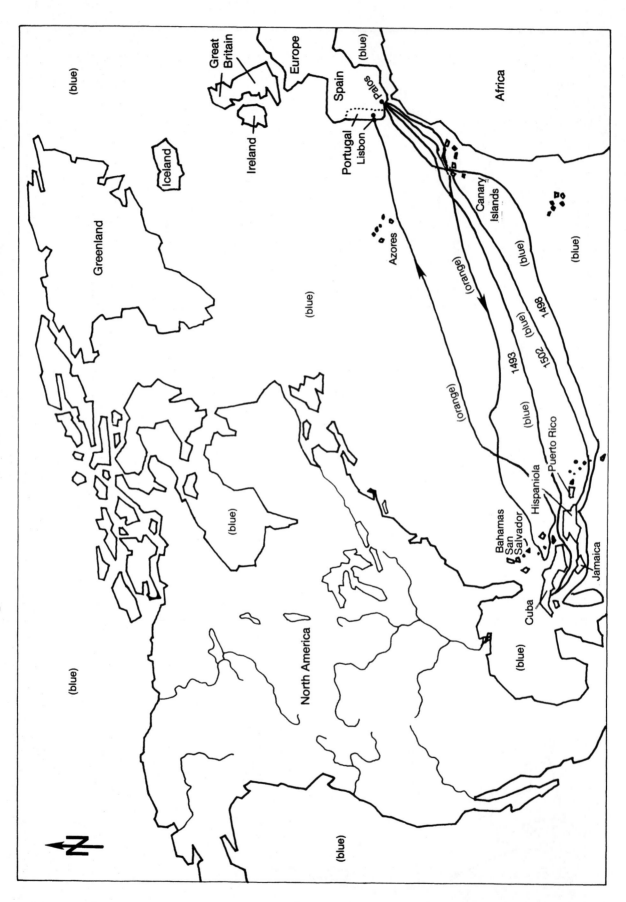

Map 3: Exploration Period

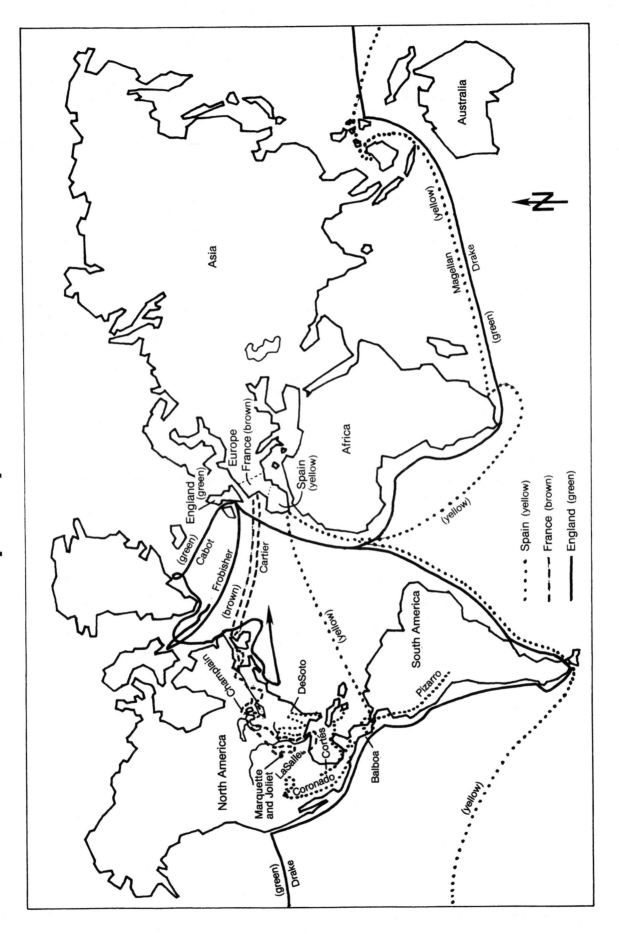

N

Asia

Australia

Magellan (yellow)

Drake (green)

Africa

Europe

France (brown)

England (green)

Spain (yellow)

(yellow)

Spain (yellow)
France (brown)
England (green)

(green)
Cabot

Frobisher (brown)

Cartier

(yellow)

South America

Pizarro

North America

Champlain

DeSoto

Marquette and Joliet

LaSalle

Coronado

Cortés

Balboa

(yellow)

(green)
Drake

Map 4: Colonization in North America

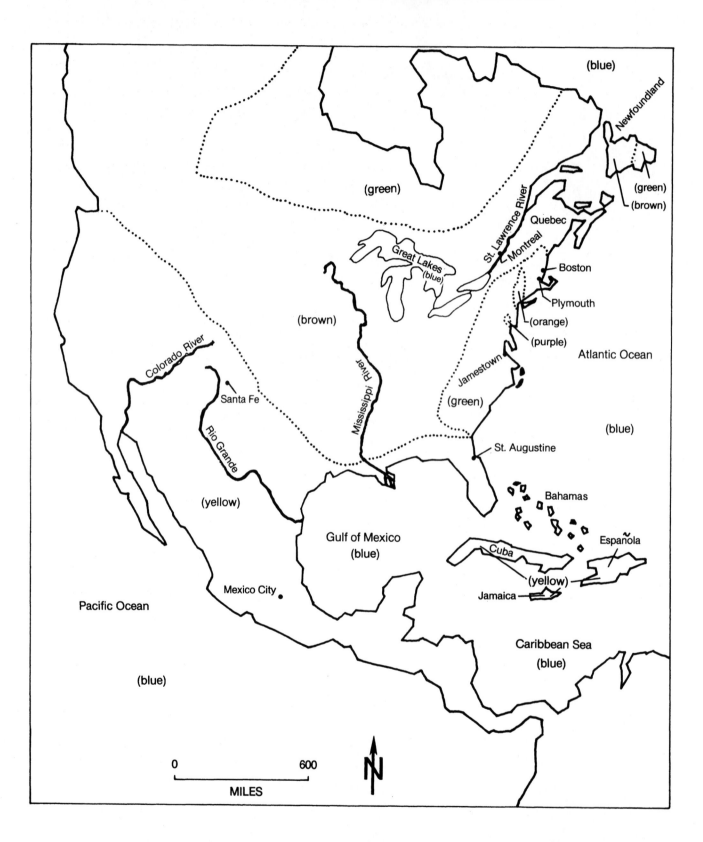

Map 5: Early English Settlement

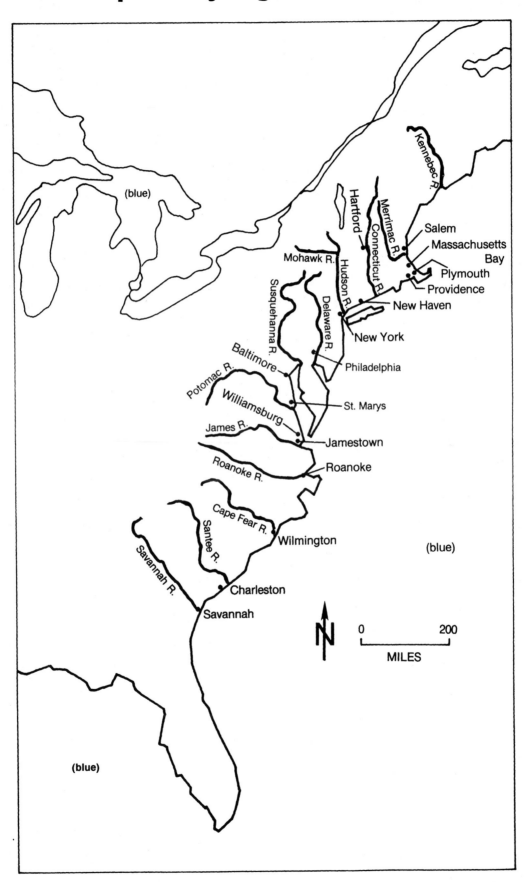

Map 6: Thirteen Colonies

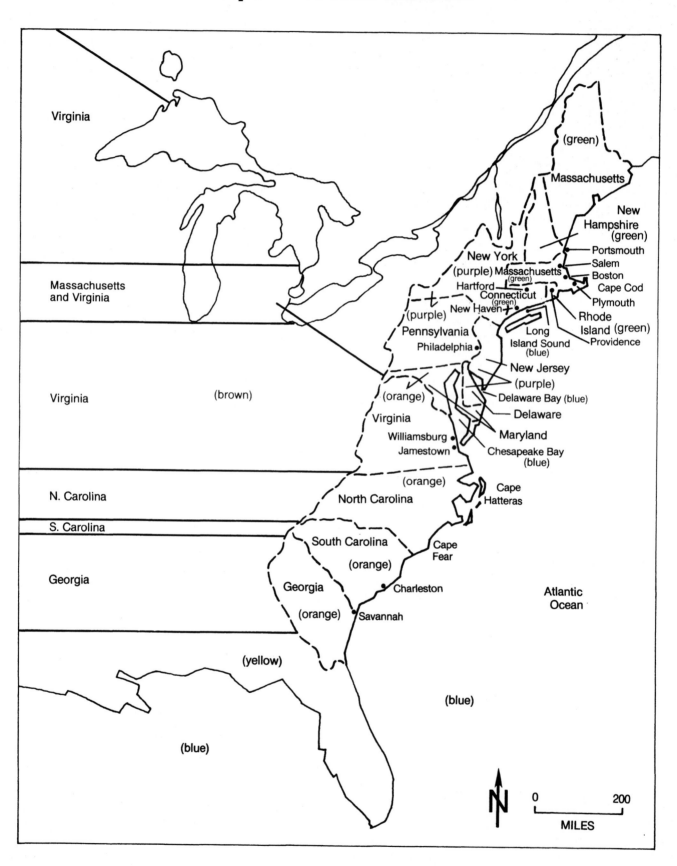

Virginia

Massachusetts
and Virginia

Virginia   (brown)

N. Carolina

S. Carolina

Georgia

(yellow)

(blue)

(green)

Massachusetts

New
Hampshire
(green)

New York
(purple)   Massachusetts
                      (green)
Hartford
Connecticut
      (green)
New Haven

(purple)

Pennsylvania
   Philadelphia

Long
Island Sound
     (blue)

Portsmouth
Salem
Boston
Cape Cod
Plymouth
Rhode
Island (green)
Providence

New Jersey
   (purple)

(orange)

Virginia

Williamsburg
Jamestown

Delaware Bay (blue)

Delaware

Maryland

Chesapeake Bay
     (blue)

(orange)

North Carolina

Cape
Hatteras

South Carolina

(orange)

Cape
Fear

Georgia

(orange)

Charleston

Savannah

Atlantic
Ocean

(blue)

N

0   200

MILES

Map 7: French and Indian War

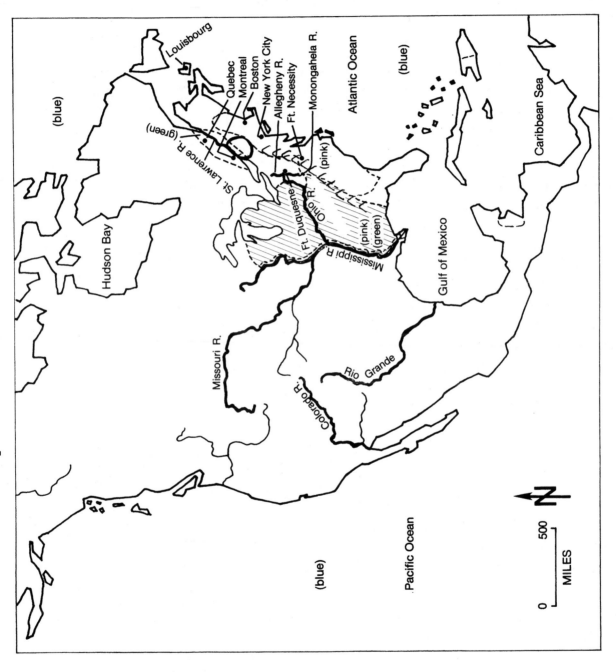

Louisbourg

Quebec
Montreal
Boston
New York City
Allegheny R.
Ft. Necessity

Monongahela R.

Atlantic Ocean

(blue)

Caribbean Sea

(blue)

St. Lawrence R. (green)

Ohio R. (pink)

Ft. Duquesne (pink)

(green)

Mississippi R.

Hudson Bay

Gulf of Mexico

Missouri R.

Rio Grande

Colorado R.

Pacific Ocean

(blue)

N

500

0

MILES

Map 8: North America in 1763

60°N

180°
170°
160°
150°
140°
130°
120°
110°
100°
90°
80°
70°
60°
50°
40°
30°
20°
10°

70°N

50°N

(blue)

Hudson Bay

(pink)

40°N

Missouri R.

St. Lawrence R.

Ft. Pitt

Pacific Ocean

30°N

(yellow)

Ohio R.

Atlantic Ocean
(blue)

Mississippi R.

(pink)

(blue)

20°N

(pink)

Haiti

(yellow)

Gulf of Mexico

(green)

(blue)

(pink)

Caribbean Sea

10°N

0   500
MILES

N

Map 9: American Revolution

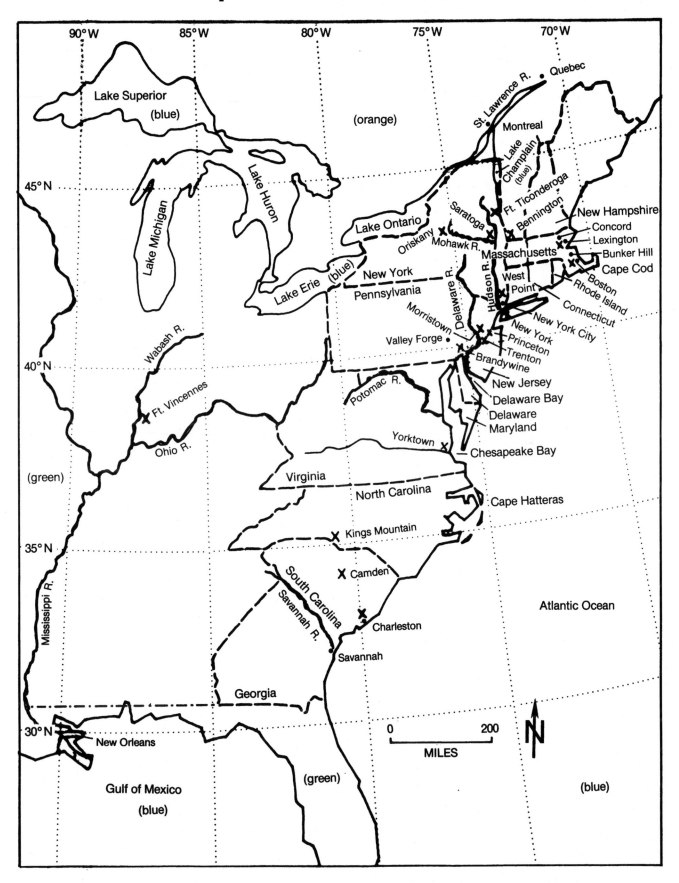

Map 10: Thirteen States and the Constitution

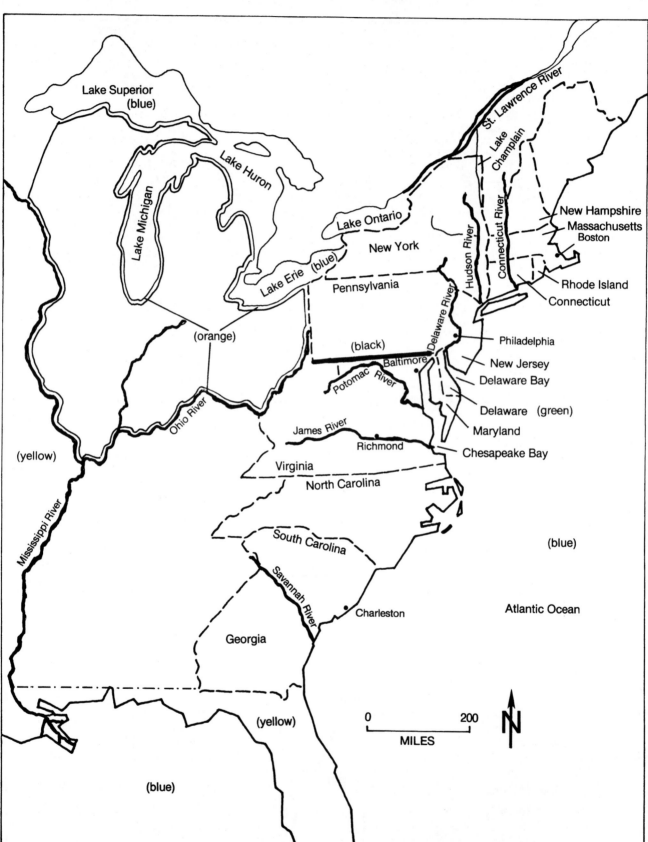

Map 11: Louisiana Purchase and Western Exploration

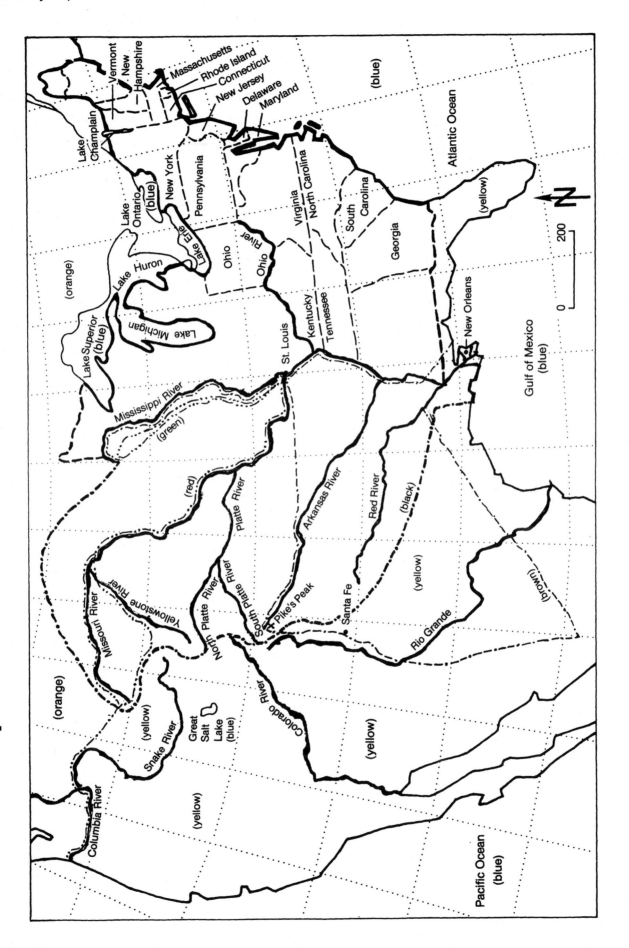

Map 12: War of 1812

(pink)

(pink)

Lake Superior
(blue)

Quebec

Montreal
St. Lawrence River

Lake Michigan

Lake Huron

Lake Ontario

Lake Champlain
(blue)

Plattsburg X

New Hampshire

York

(blue)

New York

Vermont

Massachusetts

Thames

Lake Erie

Detroit
X

Erie

New York City

Boston
Rhode Island
Connecticut

Tippecanoe

Tippecanoe River

Wabash River X

Ohio

Pennsylvania

New Jersey

Potomac River

Baltimore X

Ft. McHenry

Ohio River

Washington, D.C. X

Delaware

Maryland

Kentucky

Virginia

Chesapeake Bay

Mississippi River

Tennessee

North Carolina

(black)

Savannah River

South Carolina

Alabama River

X Horseshoe Bend

Charleston

Savannah

Louisiana

Georgia

Atlantic Ocean

Lake Pontchartrain

(blue)

New Orleans

(yellow)

Gulf of Mexico

(blue)

0   200
MILES

N

Map 13: Settlement of Northwest Territory

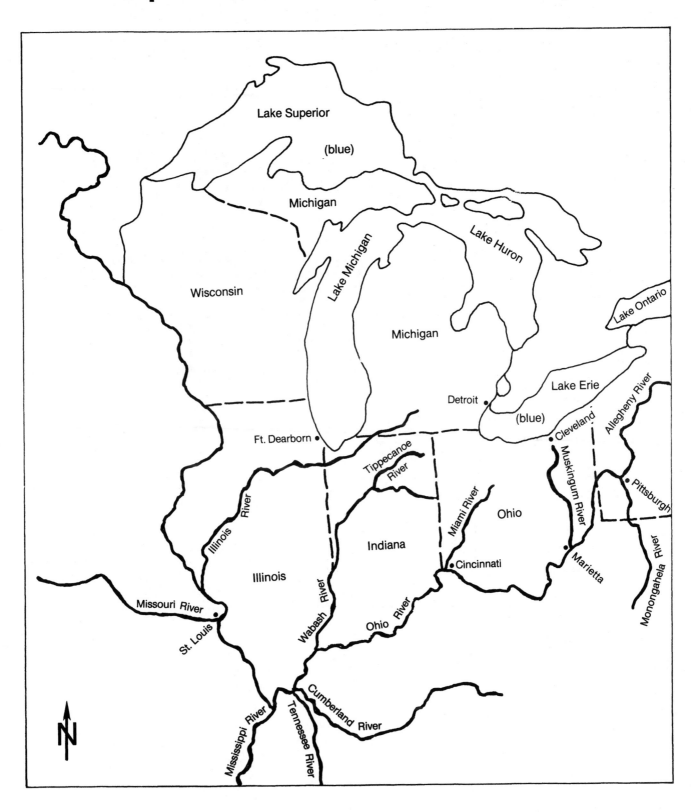

Lake Superior

(blue)

Michigan

Lake Huron

Lake Michigan

Wisconsin

Michigan

Lake Ontario

Lake Erie

Detroit

(blue)

Cleveland

Allegheny River

Ft. Dearborn

Tippecanoe River

Muskingum River

Pittsburgh

Illinois River

Miami River

Ohio

Indiana

Monongahela River

Illinois

Cincinnati

Marietta

Missouri River

Wabash River

Ohio River

St. Louis

Cumberland River

Mississippi River

Tennessee River

N

Map 14: Expansion of United States to 1833

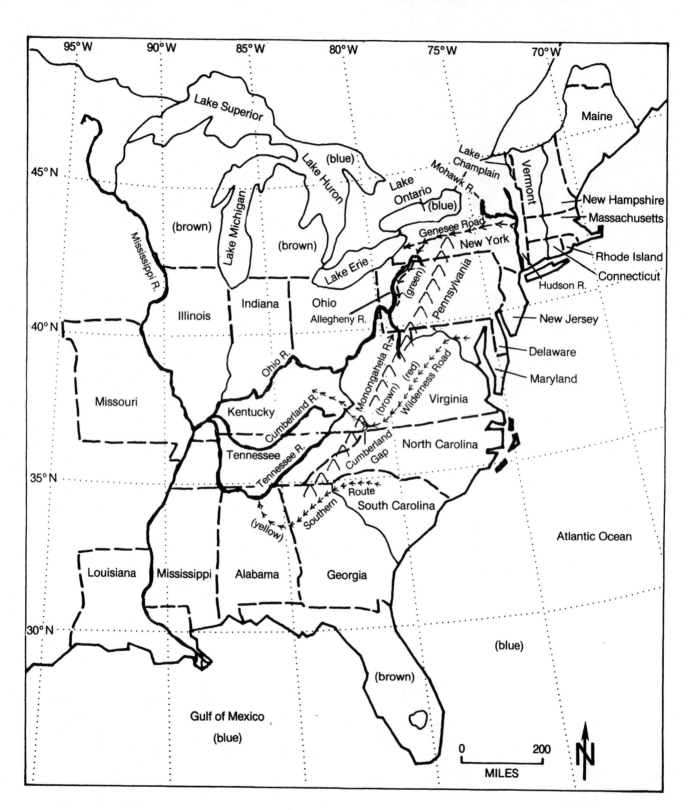

Map 15: United States Before the Civil War

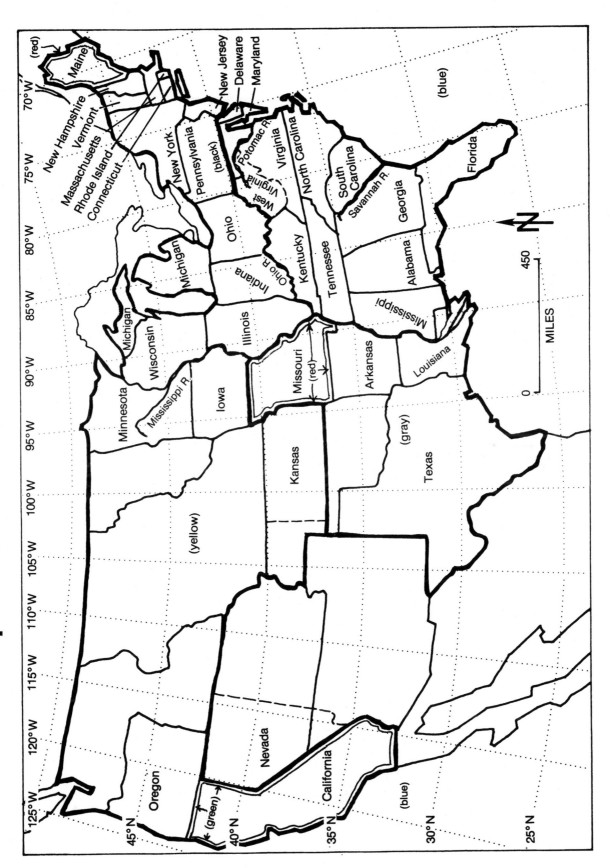

Maine (red)

New Hampshire
Vermont
Massachusetts
Rhode Island
Connecticut

New Jersey
Delaware
Maryland

New York

Pennsylvania
(black)

Potomac R.

West Virginia

Virginia

North Carolina

South Carolina

Savannah R.

Georgia

Florida

(blue)

Ohio

Indiana

Ohio R.

Kentucky

Tennessee

Alabama

Mississippi

Michigan

Michigan

Wisconsin

Illinois

Minnesota

Mississippi R.

Iowa

Missouri
(red)

Kansas

Arkansas

Louisiana

Texas

(gray)

(yellow)

Nevada

Oregon

California

(green)

(blue)

N

MILES

0   450

125°W 120°W 115°W 110°W 105°W 100°W 95°W 90°W 85°W 80°W 75°W 70°W

45°N
40°N
35°N
30°N
25°N

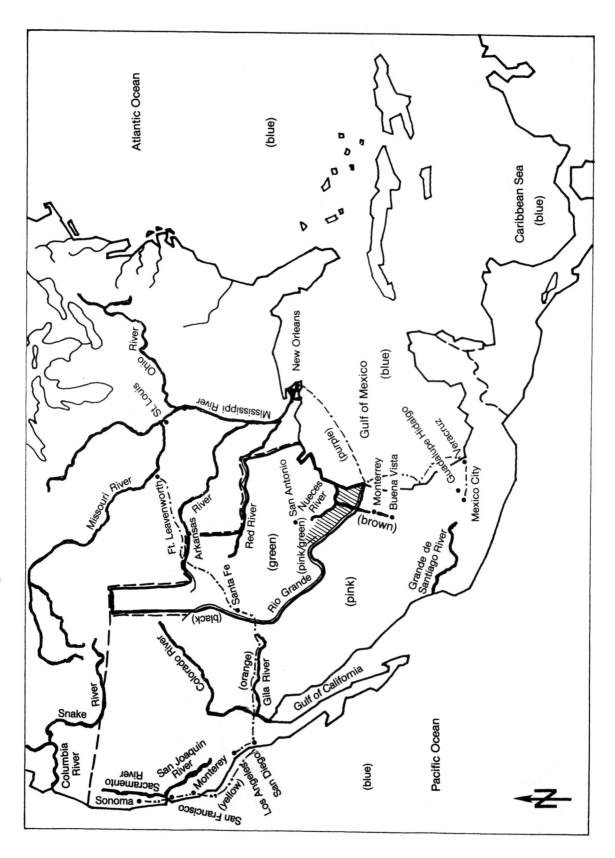

Map 16: Texas and the Mexican War

Map 17: Territorial Acquisitions

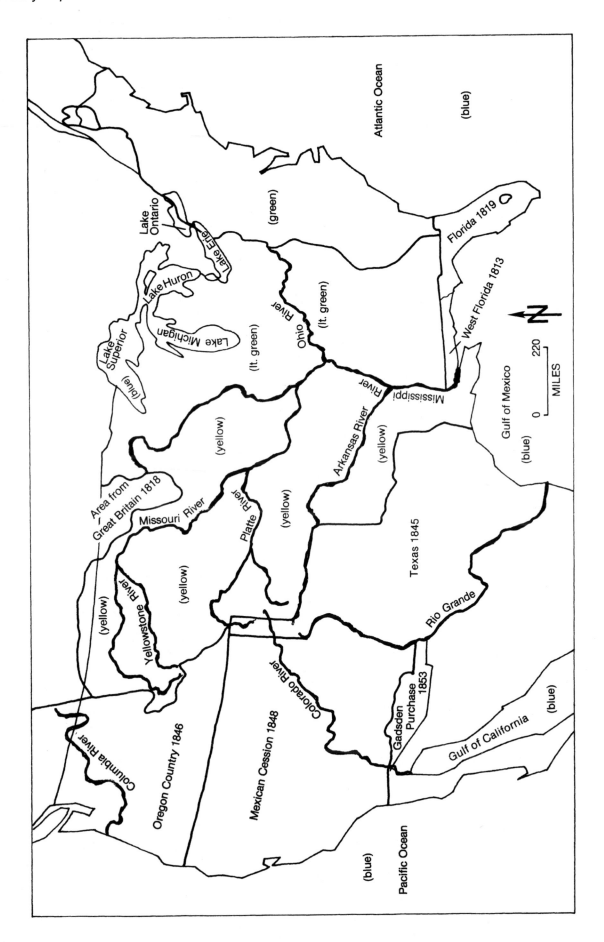

Atlantic Ocean

(blue)

(green)

Lake Ontario

Lake Erie

Lake Huron

Lake Superior

(blue)

Lake Michigan

(lt. green)

Ohio River

(lt. green)

Florida 1819

West Florida 1813

N

220

MILES

0

Gulf of Mexico

(blue)

Mississippi River

Arkansas River

(yellow)

(yellow)

(yellow)

Area from Great Britain 1818

Missouri River

Platte River

(yellow)

Texas 1845

Yellowstone River

(yellow)

Rio Grande

(yellow)

Oregon Country 1846

Mexican Cession 1848

Colorado River

Gadsden Purchase 1853

Columbia River

Gulf of California

(blue)

Pacific Ocean

(blue)

Map 18: The Way West

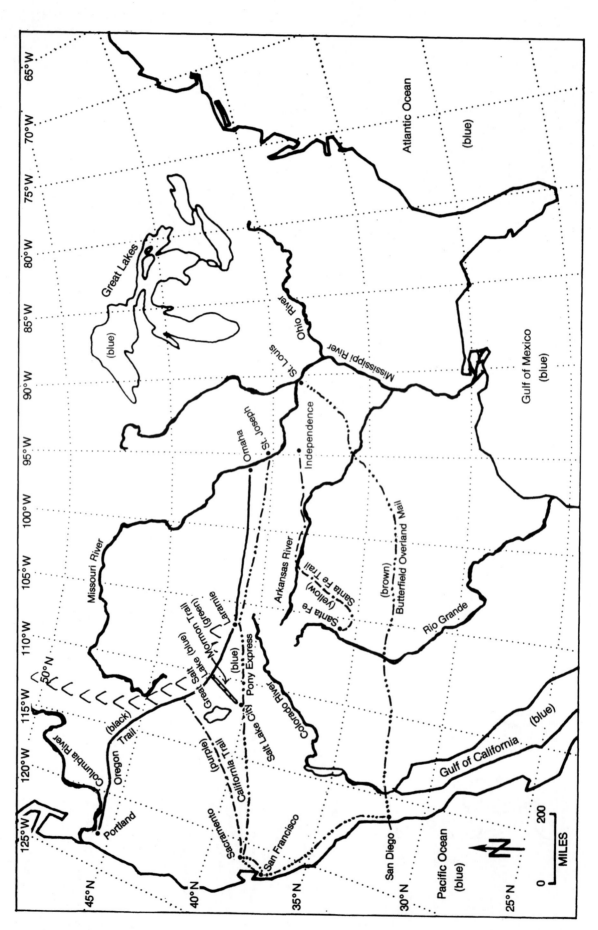

Great Lakes
(blue)

Atlantic Ocean
(blue)

Ohio River

Mississippi River

St. Louis

Gulf of Mexico
(blue)

Omaha

St. Joseph

Independence

Arkansas River

Santa Fe Trail
(yellow)

Santa Fe

Butterfield Overland Mail
(brown)

Rio Grande

Missouri River

Laramie

Mormon Trail
(green)

Great Salt
Lake (blue)

Salt Lake City

Pony Express
(blue)

California Trail
(purple)

Colorado River

Oregon
Trail
(black)

Columbia River

Portland

Sacramento

San Francisco

San Diego

Gulf of California
(blue)

Pacific Ocean
(blue)

N

MILES
0   200

Map 19: Mining Regions and Cattle Trails of the Old West

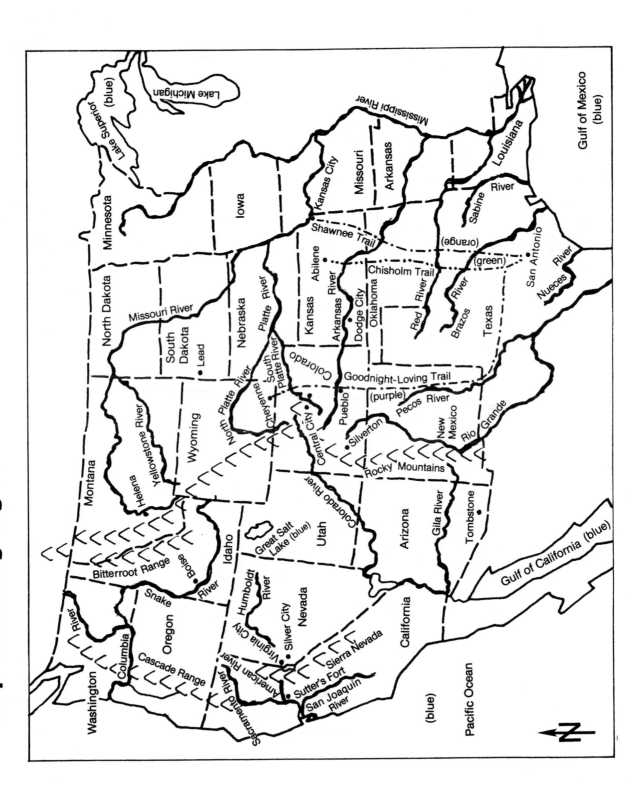

Map 20: War Between the States

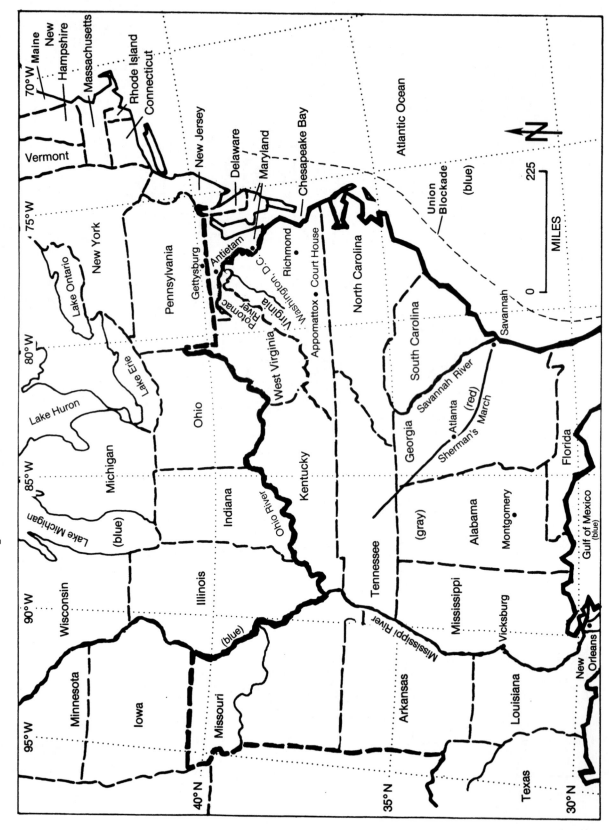

Map 21: Overseas America 1867–1940

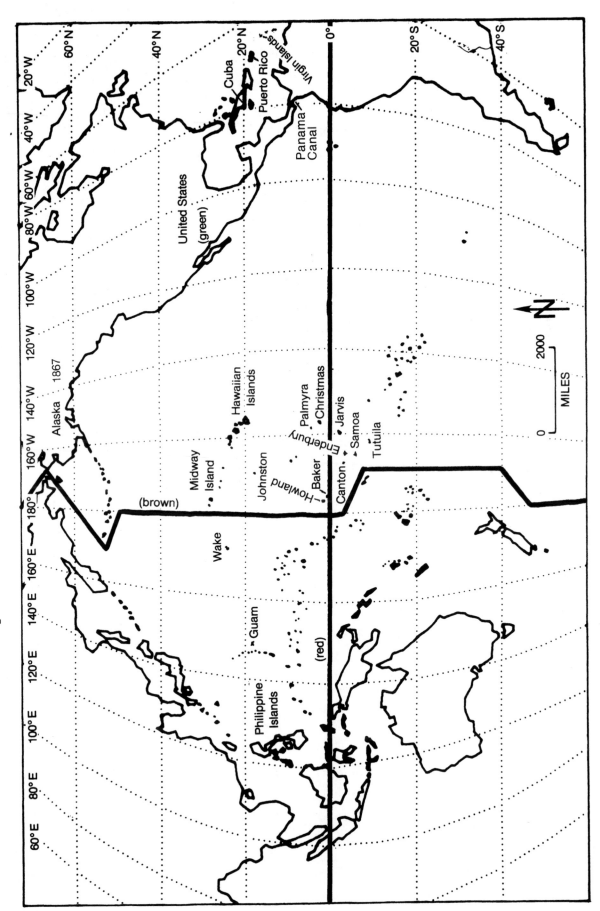

- Cuba
- Puerto Rico
- Virgin Islands
- Panama Canal
- United States (green)
- 1867
- Alaska
- Hawaiian Islands
- Palmyra
- Christmas
- Jarvis
- Samoa
- Tutuila
- Enderbury
- Midway Island
- (brown)
- Johnston
- Baker
- Howland
- Canton
- Wake
- (red)
- Guam
- Philippine Islands

MILES
0   2000

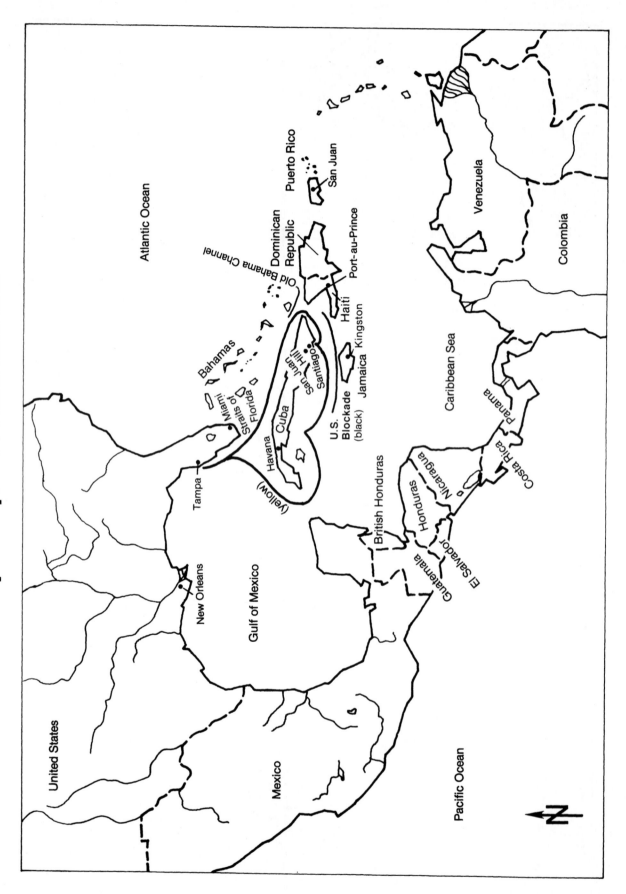

Map 22: Spanish-American War

United States

New Orleans

Tampa

Mexico

Gulf of Mexico

Florida
Straits of
Miami

Bahamas

Atlantic Ocean

(Yellow)

Havana

Cuba

San Juan Hill

Santiago

U.S.
Blockade
(black)

Jamaica Kingston

Haiti

Port-au-Prince

Old Bahama Channel

Dominican
Republic

Puerto Rico

San Juan

Venezuela

Colombia

Caribbean Sea

British Honduras

Guatemala

El Salvador

Honduras

Nicaragua

Costa Rica

Panama

Pacific Ocean

N

Map 23: World War I

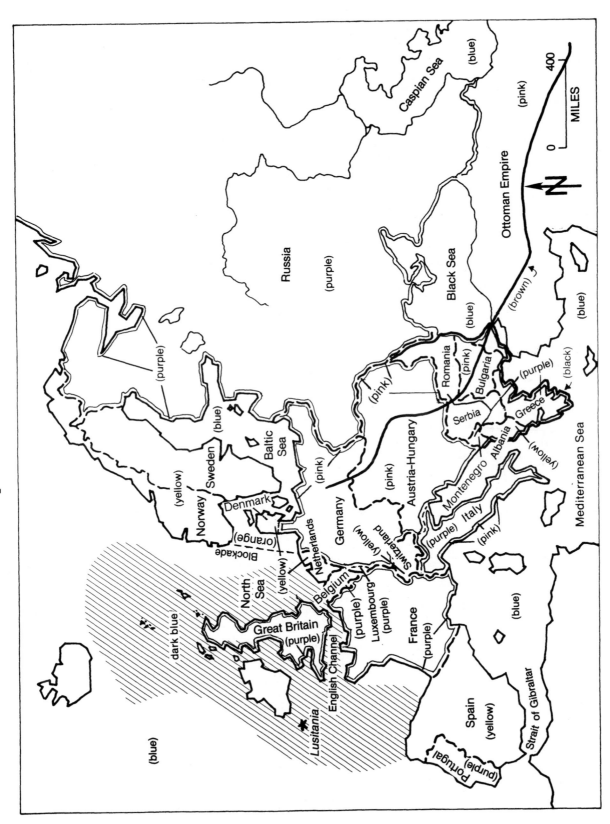

Caspian Sea (blue)

Ottoman Empire (pink)

Russia (purple)

Black Sea (blue)

(brown)

(purple)

Romania (pink)

Bulgaria

Serbia

Greece (black)

Austria-Hungary (pink)

Montenegro

Albania (yellow)

Italy (pink)

(purple)

Mediterranean Sea

(pink)

(blue)

Sweden (blue)

Baltic Sea

Norway (yellow)

Denmark

Germany (pink)

Switzerland (yellow)

(orange)

Blockade

Netherlands (yellow)

Belgium

Luxembourg (purple)

France (purple)

North Sea

Great Britain (purple)

English Channel

Lusitania

dark blue

(blue)

Spain (yellow)

Strait of Gibraltar

Portugal (purple)

(blue)

MILES

0   400

N

Map 24: World War II in the Pacific

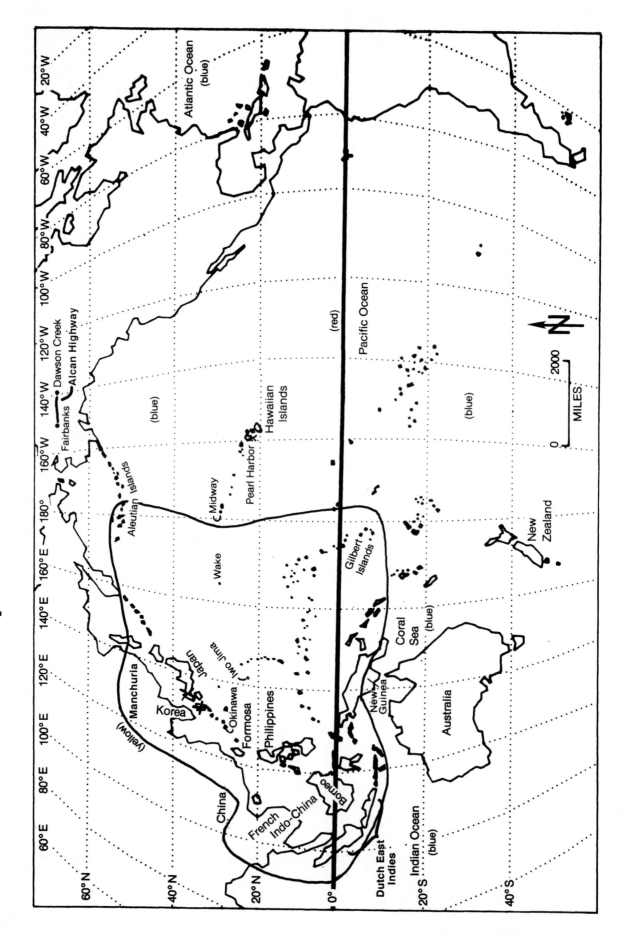

Atlantic Ocean (blue)

Dawson Creek
Alcan Highway
Fairbanks

(blue)

Pacific Ocean

(red)

Hawaiian Islands

Pearl Harbor

Midway

Aleutian Islands

Wake

(blue)

New Zealand

Gilbert Islands

Manchuria

Korea

Japan

Iwo Jima

Okinawa

Formosa

Philippines

New Guinea

Coral Sea (blue)

Australia

China

(Yellow)

French Indo-China

Borneo

Dutch East Indies

Indian Ocean (blue)

N

MILES
0   2000

60° N
40° N
20° N
0°
20° S
40° S

20° W
40° W
60° W
80° W
100° W
120° W
140° W
160° W
180°
160° E
140° E
120° E
100° E
80° E
60° E

Map 25: American Involvement in Vietnam

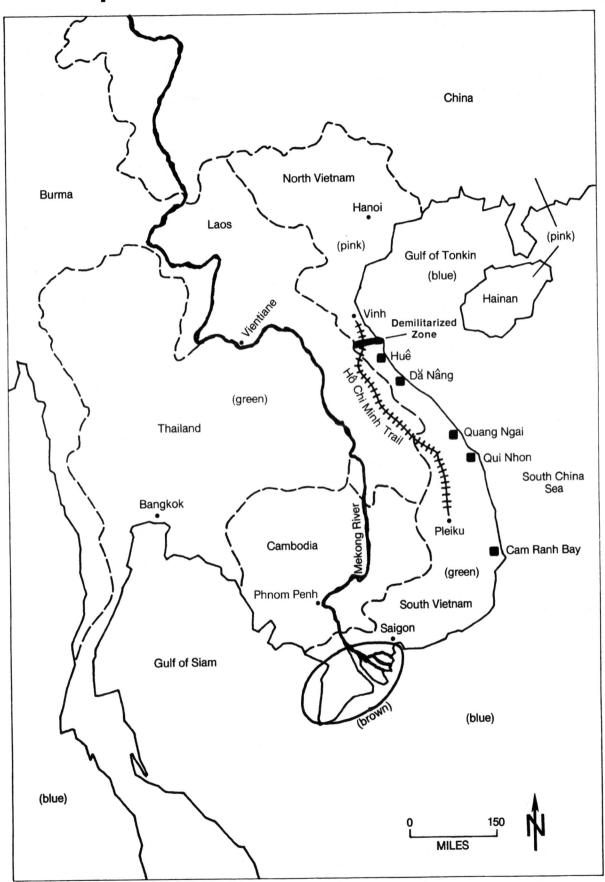

China

North Vietnam

Burma

Hanoi

Laos

(pink)

(pink)

Gulf of Tonkin

(blue)

Vientiane

Hainan

Vinh

Demilitarized
Zone

Huê

Dǎ Nâng

(green)

Hồ Chi Minh Trail

Thailand

Quang Ngai

Qui Nhon

South China
Sea

Bangkok

Mekong River

Pleiku

Cambodia

Cam Ranh Bay

(green)

Phnom Penh

South Vietnam

Saigon

Gulf of Siam

(brown)

(blue)

(blue)

0   150

N

MILES

Share Your Bright Ideas with Us!

We want to hear from you! Your valuable comments and suggestions will help us meet your current and future classroom needs.

Your name_____Date_____

School name_____Phone_____

School address_____

City_____State_____Zip_____Phone number (_____)_____

Grade level taught_____Subject area(s) taught_____Average class size_____

Where did you purchase this publication?_____

Was your salesperson knowledgeable about this product?   Yes_____   No_____

What monies were used to purchase this product?

____School supplemental budget   ____Federal/state funding   ____Personal

Please "grade" this Walch publication according to the following criteria:

Quality of service you received when purchasing ....A B C D F
Ease of use..A B C D F
Quality of content...A B C D F
Page layout ....A B C D F
Organization of material ....A B C D F
Suitability for grade level..A B C D F
Instructional value..A B C D F

COMMENTS:_____

_____

What specific supplemental materials would help you meet your current—or future—instructional needs?

_____

Have you used other Walch publications? If so, which ones?_____

May we use your comments in upcoming communications?   ____Yes   ____No

Please **FAX** this completed form to **207-772-3105**, or mail it to:

Product Development, J. Weston Walch, Publisher, P. O. Box 658, Portland, ME 04104-0658

We will send you a **FREE GIFT** as our way of thanking you for your feedback. **THANK YOU!**